math expressions

Dr. Karen C. Fuson

Watch the moose come alive in its snowy environment as you discover and solve math challenges.

Download the *Math Worlds AR* app available on Android or iOS devices.

Grade 3

Volume 1

This material is based upon work supported by the
National Science Foundation
under Grant Numbers
ESI-9816320, REC-9806020, and RED-935373.

Cover Illustration: ©Josh Brill

Printed in the U.S.A.

ISBN 978-1-328-74382-4

13 0928 26 25 24 23 22

4500846506 C D E F G

Unit 1 | Multiplication and Division with 0–5, 9, and 10

BIG IDEA 1 - Meanings of Multiplication and Division: 5s and 2s

BIG IDEA 2 - Patterns and Strategies: 9s and 10s

BIG IDEA 3 - Strategies for Factors and Products: 3s and 4s

Unit 2 | Multiplication and Division with 6s, 7s, and 8s and Multiply with Multiples of 10

BIG IDEA 1 - The Remaining Multiplications

BIG IDEA 2 - Problem Solving and Multiples of 10

Unit 3 | Multidigit Addition, Subtraction, and Multiplication

BIG IDEA 1 - Understand Place Value and Rounding

BIG IDEA 2 - Addition and Subtraction Strategies and Group to Add

BIG IDEA 3 - Ungroup to Subtract

Student Resources

Dear Family:

In this unit and the next, your child will be practicing basic multiplications and divisions. *Math Expressions* uses studying, practicing, and testing of the basic multiplications and divisions in class. Your child also should practice at home.

Homework Helper Your child will have math homework almost every day. He or she needs a Homework Helper. The helper may be anyone — you, an older brother or sister (or other family member), a neighbor, or a friend. Please decide who the main Homework Helper will be and ask your child to tell the teacher tomorrow. Make a specific time for homework and give your child a quiet place to work.

Study Plans Each day your child will fill out a study plan, indicating which basic multiplications and divisions he or she will study that evening. When your child has finished studying (practicing), his or her Homework Helper should sign the study plan.

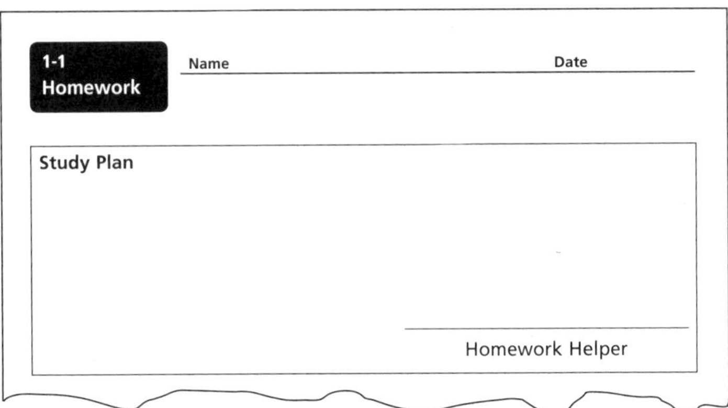
1-1 Homework
Name Date
Study Plan
Homework Helper

Practice Charts Each time a new number is introduced, students' homework will include a practice chart. To practice, students can cover the products with a finger or pencil. They will say the multiplications, sliding the finger or pencil down the column to see each product after saying it. Students can also start with the last problem in a column and slide up. It is important that your child studies count-bys and multiplications at least 5 minutes every night. Your child should study each division on the Mixed Up column by covering the first factor.

Keep all materials in a special place.

	In Order	Mixed Up
5s	$1 \times 5 = 5$	$9 \times 5 = 45$
	$2 \times 5 = 10$	$5 \times 5 = 25$
	$3 \times 5 = 15$	$2 \times 5 = 10$
	$4 \times 5 = 20$	$7 \times 5 = 35$
	$5 \times 5 = 25$	$4 \times 5 = 20$
	$6 \times 5 = 30$	$6 \times 5 = 30$
	$7 \times 5 = 35$	$10 \times 5 = 50$
	$8 \times 5 = 40$	$8 \times 5 = 40$
	$9 \times 5 = 45$	$1 \times 5 = 5$
	$10 \times 5 = 50$	$3 \times 5 = 15$

To help students understand the concept of multiplication, the *Math Expressions* program presents three ways to think about multiplication.

- **Repeated groups**: Multiplication can be used to find the total in repeated groups of the same size. In early lessons, students circle the group size in repeated-groups equations to help keep track of which factor is the group size and which is the number of groups.

4 groups of bananas

$4 \times (3) = 3 + 3 + 3 + 3 = 12$

- **Arrays**: Multiplication can be used to find the total number of items in an *array*—an arrangement of objects into rows and columns.

5 columns

2 rows

2-by-5 array

2 rows of pennies $= 2 \times 5 = 10$

- **Area**: Multiplication can be used to find the area of a rectangle

3 units

6 units

Area: 3 units × 6 units = 18 square units

Please contact me if you have any questions or comments.

Thank you.

Sincerely,
Your child's teacher

Estimada familia:

En esta unidad y en la que sigue, su niño practicará multiplicaciones y divisiones básicas. *Math Expressions* usa en la clase el estudio, la práctica y la evaluación de las multiplicaciones y divisiones básicas. También su niño debe practicar en casa.

Ayudante de tareas Su niño tendrá tarea de matemáticas casi a diario y necesitará un ayudante para hacer sus tareas. Ese ayudante puede ser cualquier persona: usted, un hermano o hermana mayor, otro familiar, un vecino o un amigo. Por favor decida quién será esta persona y pida a su niño que se lo diga a su maestro mañana. Designe un tiempo específico para la tarea y un lugar para trabajar sin distracciones.

Planes de estudio Todos los días su niño va a completar un plan de estudio, que indica cuáles multiplicaciones y divisiones debe estudiar esa noche. Cuando su niño haya terminado de estudiar (practicar), la persona que lo ayude debe firmar el plan de estudio.

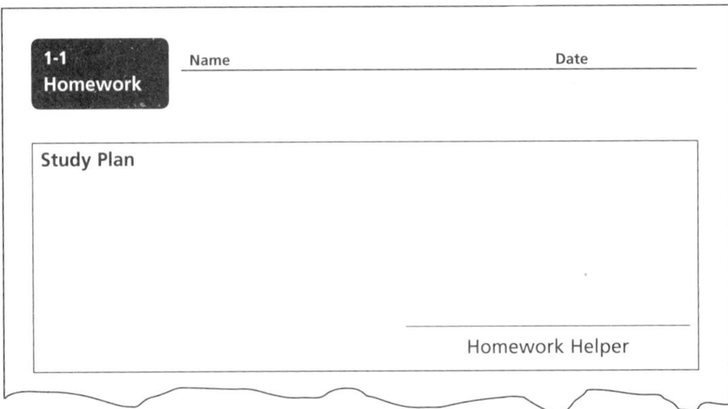
1-1 Homework

Name Date

Study Plan

Homework Helper

Tablas de práctica Cada vez que se presente un número nuevo, la tarea de los estudiantes incluirá una tabla de práctica. Para practicar, los estudiantes pueden cubrir los productos con un dedo o lápiz.Los niños dicen la multiplicación y deslizan el dedo o lápiz hacia abajo para revelar el producto después de decirlo. También pueden empezar con el último problema de la columna y deslizar el lápiz o el papel hacia arriba. Es importante que su niño practique el conteo y la multiplicación por lo menos 5 minutos cada noche. Su niño debe estudiar cada división en la columna de Desordenados cubriendo el primer factor.

	In Order	Mixed Up
5s	1 × 5 = 5	9 × 5 = 45
	2 × 5 = 10	5 × 5 = 25
	3 × 5 = 15	2 × 5 = 10
	4 × 5 = 20	7 × 5 = 35
	5 × 5 = 25	4 × 5 = 20
	6 × 5 = 30	6 × 5 = 30
	7 × 5 = 35	10 × 5 = 50
	8 × 5 = 40	8 × 5 = 40
	9 × 5 = 45	1 × 5 = 5
	10 × 5 = 50	3 × 5 = 15

Guarde todos los materiales.

Carta a la familia | Un vistazo general al contenido

Para ayudar a los estudiantes a comprender el concepto de la multiplicación, el programa *Math Expressions* presenta tres maneras de pensar en la multiplicación. Éstas se describen a continuación.

- **Grupos repetidos**: La multiplicación se puede usar para hallar el total con grupos del mismo tamaño que se repiten. Cuando empiezan a trabajar con ecuaciones de grupos repetidos, los estudiantes rodean con un círculo el tamaño del grupo en las ecuaciones, para recordar cuál factor representa el tamaño del grupo y cuál representa el número de grupos.

4 grupos de bananas

$4 \times \textcircled{3} = 3 + 3 + 3 + 3 = 12$

- **Matrices**: Se puede usar la multiplicación para hallar el número total de objetos en una *matriz*, es decir, una disposición de objetos en filas y columnas.

5 columnas

2 filas

matriz de 2 por 5

2 filas de monedas de un centavo $= 2 \times 5 = 10$

- **Área**: Se puede usar la multiplicación para hallar el área de un rectángulo.

3 unidades

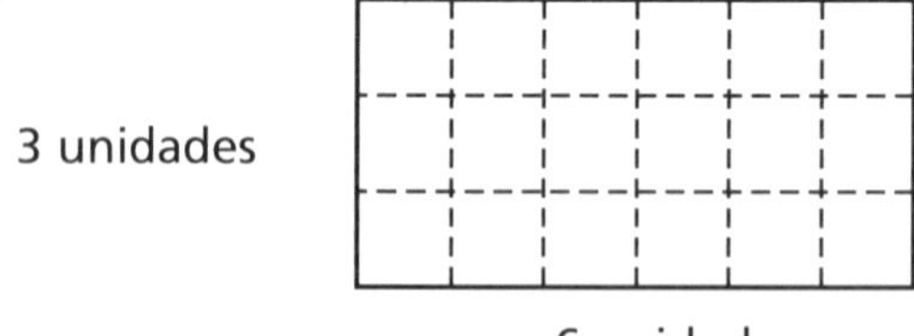

6 unidades

Área: 3 unidades $\times$ 6 unidades = 18 unidades cuadradas

Si tiene alguna duda o algún comentario, por favor comuníquese conmigo. Gracias.

Atentamente,
El maestro de su niño

area

Associative Property of Multiplication

array

column

Associative Property of Addition

Commutative Property of Addition

The property that states that changing the way in which factors are grouped does not change the product.

Example:

$(2 \times 3) \times 4 = 2 \times (3 \times 4)$

$6 \times 4 = 2 \times 12$

$24 = 24$

The total number of square units that cover a figure.

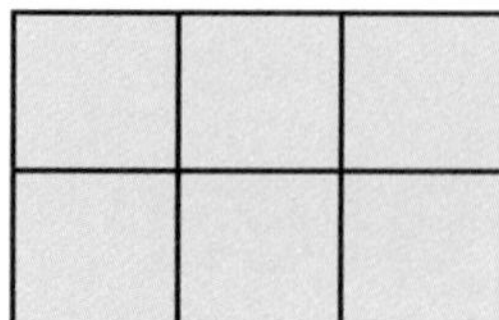

Example:

The area of the rectangle is 6 square units.

A part of a table or array that contains items arranged vertically.

An arrangement of objects, pictures, or numbers in columns and rows.

The property that states that changing the order of addends does not change the sum.

Example:

$3 + 7 = 7 + 3$

$10 = 10$

The property that states that changing the way in which addends are grouped does not change the sum.

Example:

$(2 + 3) + 1 = 2 + (3 + 1)$

$5 + 1 = 2 + 4$

$6 = 6$

Commutative Property of Multiplication	**division**
Distributive Property	**divisor**
dividend	**equal groups**

The mathematical operation that separates an amount into smaller equal groups to find the number of groups or the number in each group.

Example:

$12 \div 3 = 4$ is a division number sentence.

The property that states that changing the order of factors does not change the product.

Example:

$5 \times 4 = 4 \times 5$

$20 = 20$

The number that you divide by in division.

Example:

$12 \div 3 = 4$ $3\overline{)12}$ (quotient 4)

divisor   divisor

You can multiply a sum by a number, or multiply each addend by the number and add the products; the result is the same.

Example:

$3 \times (2 + 4) = (3 \times 2) + (3 \times 4)$

$3 \times 6 = 6 + 12$

$18 = 18$

Two or more groups with the same number of items in each group.

The number that is divided in division.

Example:

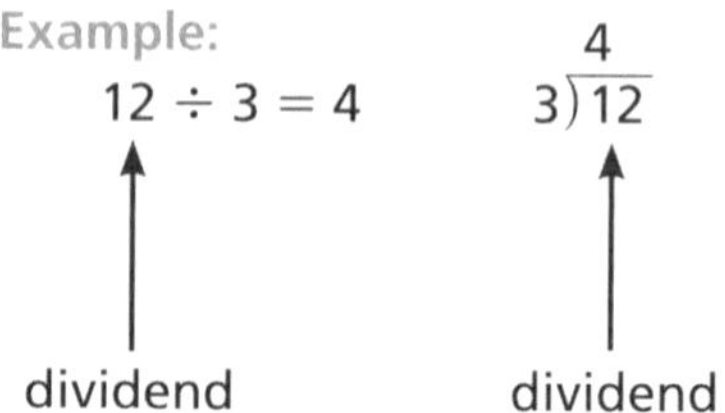

equation

function table

even number

Identity Property of Addition

factor

Identity Property of Multiplication

A table of ordered pairs that shows a function.

For every input number, there is only one possible output number.

Rule: add 2	
Input	Output
1	3
2	4
3	5
4	6

A mathematical sentence with an equals sign.

Examples:

11 + 22 = 33

75 − 25 = 50

If 0 is added to a number, the sum equals that number.

Example:

3 + 0 = 3

A whole number that is a multiple of 2. The ones digit in an even number is 0, 2, 4, 6, or 8.

The product of 1 and any number equals that number.

Example:

10 × 1 = 10

Any of the numbers that are multiplied to give a product.

Example:

4 × 5 = 20

factor factor product

(>) is greater than

odd number

(<) is less than

pictograph

multiplication

product

A whole number that is not a multiple of 2. The ones digit in an odd number is 1, 3, 5, 7, or 9.

A symbol used to compare two numbers.

Example:

$6 > 5$

6 *is greater than* 5.

A graph that uses pictures or symbols to represent data.

Favorite Ice Cream Flavors

Peanut Butter Crunch	🍦 half 🍦
Cherry Vanilla	🍦 🍦 🍦
Chocolate	🍦 🍦 🍦 🍦 🍦

Each 🍦 stands for 4 votes.

A symbol used to compare two numbers.

Example:

$5 < 6$

5 *is less than* 6.

The answer when you multiply numbers.

Example:

$4 \times 7 = 28$

factor factor product

A mathematical operation that combines equal groups.

Example:

$4 \times 3 = 12$

factor factor product

$\underbrace{3 + 3 + 3 + 3}_{\text{4 times}} = 12$

quotient

variable

row

Zero Property of Multiplication

square unit

A letter or symbol used to represent an unknown number in an algebraic expression or equation.

Example:

$2 + n$

n is a variable.

The answer when you divide numbers.

Example:

$35 \div 7 = 5$ ← quotient

$7\overline{)35}$ with 5 above ← quotient

If 0 is multiplied by a number, the product is 0.

Example:

$3 \times 0 = 0$

A part of a table or array that contains items arranged horizontally.

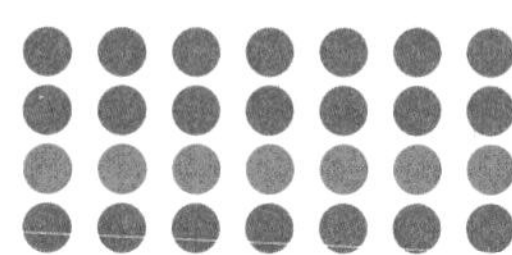

A unit of area equal to the area of a square with one-unit sides.

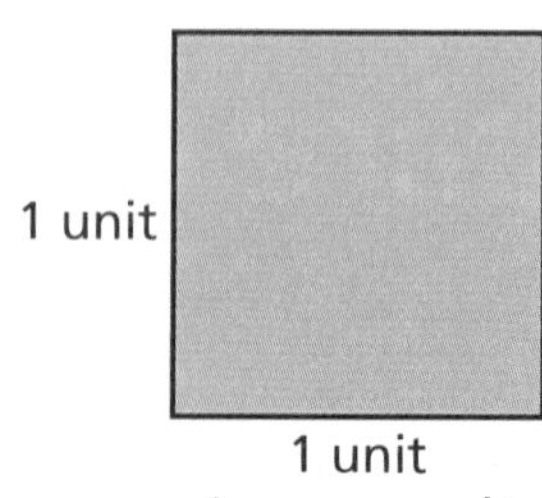

Name ____________________

Explore Equal Shares Drawings

Here is a problem with repeated groups. Read the problem, and think about how you would solve it.

Ms. Thomas bought 4 bags of oranges. Each bag contained 5 oranges. How many oranges did she buy in all?

You could also find the answer to this problem by making an equal shares drawing.

Think:

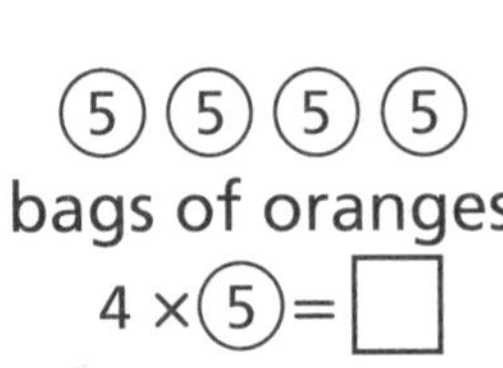

Equal Shares Drawing

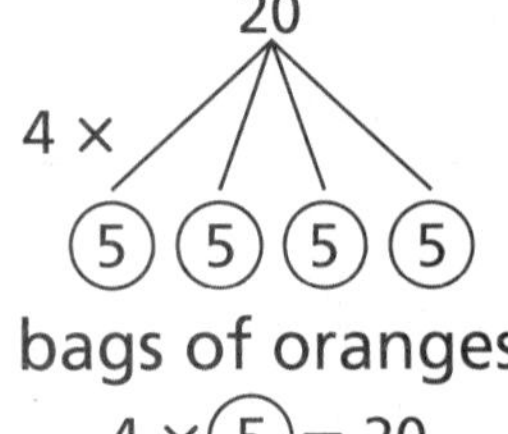

4 × 5 = 20

Make an equal shares drawing to solve each problem.

Show your work.

9 Ms. González bought 6 boxes of pencils. There were 5 pencils in each box. How many pencils did she buy in all?

____

10 Mr. Franken made lunch for his 9 nieces and nephews. He put 5 carrot sticks on each of their plates. How many carrot sticks did he use in all?

____

VOCABULARY
function table

PATH to FLUENCY Practice with Equal Groups

Complete each function table.

11

Number of Tricycles	Number of Wheels
1	
2	
3	
4	
5	

12

Number of Rabbits	Number of Ears
1	
2	
3	
4	
5	

13

Number of Cars	Number of Wheels
1	
2	
3	
4	
5	

14

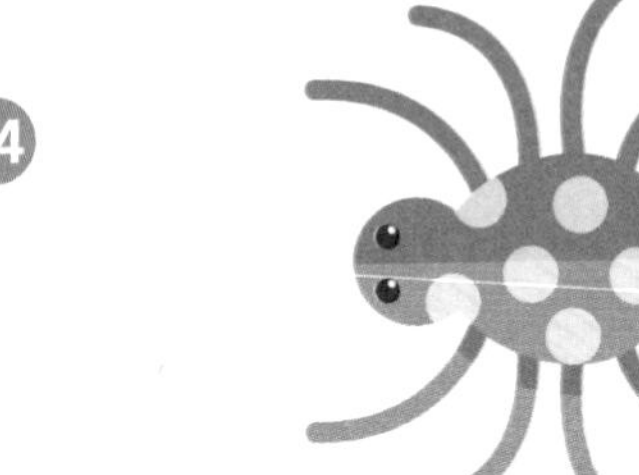

Number of Spiders	Number of Legs
1	
2	
3	
4	
5	

Check Understanding

Draw an equal shares drawing to find the number of markers in 8 packages of markers with 5 markers in each package.

Dear Family:

Over the next few weeks your child will bring home a Practice Chart for each new number to practice multiplications and divisions. Other practice materials will also come home:

- **Home Study Sheets:** A Home Study Sheet includes 3 or 4 practice charts on one page. Your child can use the Home Study Sheets to practice all the count-bys, multiplications, and divisions for a number or to practice just the ones he or she doesn't know for that number. The Homework Helper uses the sheet to test (or retest) your child by giving problems. The Homework Helper should check with your child to see which basic multiplications or divisions he or she is ready to be tested on. The helper should mark any missed problems lightly with a pencil.

  If your child gets all the answers in a column correct, the helper should sign that column on the Home Signature Sheet. When signatures are on all the columns of the Home Signature Sheet, your child should bring the sheet to school.

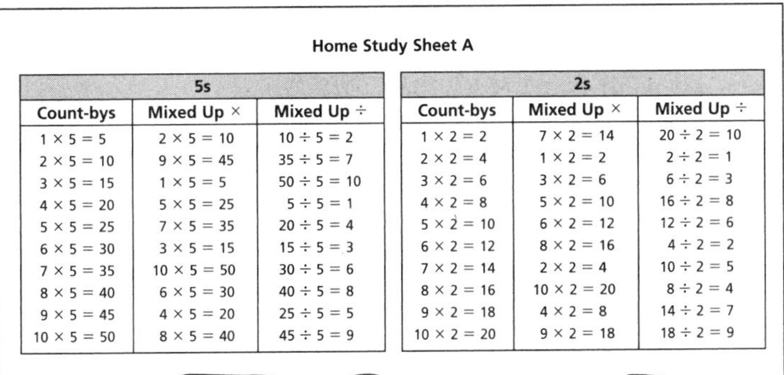

Home Study Sheet A

5s			2s		
Count-bys	Mixed Up ×	Mixed Up ÷	Count-bys	Mixed Up ×	Mixed Up ÷
1 × 5 = 5	2 × 5 = 10	10 ÷ 5 = 2	1 × 2 = 2	7 × 2 = 14	20 ÷ 2 = 10
2 × 5 = 10	9 × 5 = 45	35 ÷ 5 = 7	2 × 2 = 4	1 × 2 = 2	2 ÷ 2 = 1
3 × 5 = 15	1 × 5 = 5	50 ÷ 5 = 10	3 × 2 = 6	3 × 2 = 6	6 ÷ 2 = 3
4 × 5 = 20	5 × 5 = 25	5 ÷ 5 = 1	4 × 2 = 8	5 × 2 = 10	16 ÷ 2 = 8
5 × 5 = 25	7 × 5 = 35	20 ÷ 5 = 4	5 × 2 = 10	6 × 2 = 12	12 ÷ 2 = 6
6 × 5 = 30	3 × 5 = 15	15 ÷ 5 = 3	6 × 2 = 12	8 × 2 = 16	4 ÷ 2 = 2
7 × 5 = 35	10 × 5 = 50	30 ÷ 5 = 6	7 × 2 = 14	2 × 2 = 4	10 ÷ 2 = 5
8 × 5 = 40	6 × 5 = 30	40 ÷ 5 = 8	8 × 2 = 16	10 × 2 = 20	8 ÷ 2 = 4
9 × 5 = 45	4 × 5 = 20	25 ÷ 5 = 5	9 × 2 = 18	4 × 2 = 8	14 ÷ 2 = 7
10 × 5 = 50	8 × 5 = 40	45 ÷ 5 = 9	10 × 2 = 20	9 × 2 = 18	18 ÷ 2 = 9

Children practice by covering the answers with their finger or a pencil and sliding down their finger or pencil to check each answer as soon as they say it.

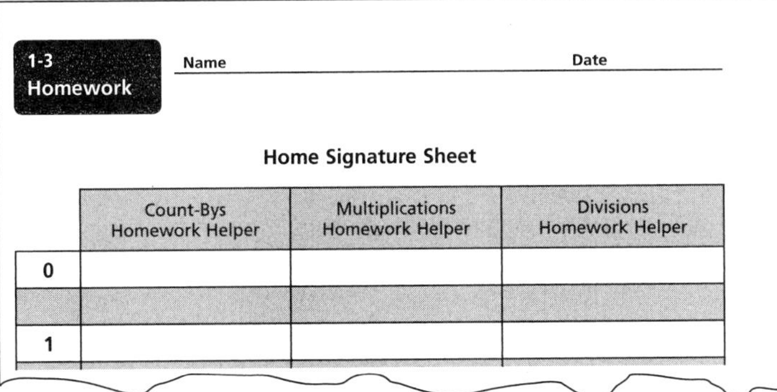

1-3 Homework

Name ________________ Date ________

Home Signature Sheet

	Count-Bys Homework Helper	Multiplications Homework Helper	Divisions Homework Helper
0			
1			

Put all practice materials in the folder your child brought home today.

- **Home Check Sheets:** A Home Check Sheet includes columns of 20 multiplications and divisions in mixed order. These sheets can be used to test your child's fluency with basic multiplications and divisions.
- **Strategy Cards:** Your child should use the Strategy Cards to practice multiplication and division by trying to answer the problem on the front. That card is put into one of three piles: *Know Quickly, Know Slowly*, and *Do Not Know*. The *Know Slowly* and *Do Not Know* cards are practiced until they are known quickly.

Sample Multiplication Card

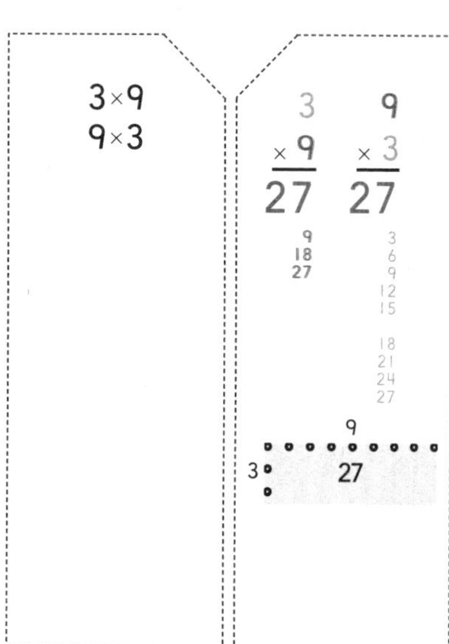

Sample Division Card

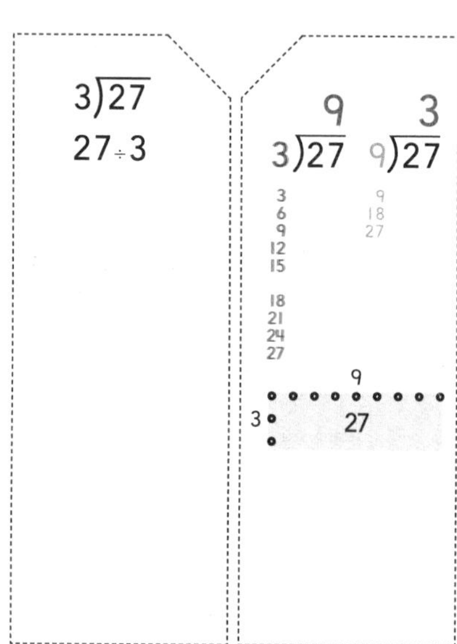

Ask your child to show you these materials and explain how they are used. Your child should practice what they do not know every day.

Please contact me if you have any questions or comments.

Thank you.

Sincerely,
Your child's teacher

Keep all materials in the Home Practice Folder. Keep the folder in a special place.

Estimada familia:

Durante las próximas semanas su niño llevará a casa una tabla de práctica para cada número nuevo para practicar multiplicaciones y divisiones. Otros materiales de práctica también se llevará a casa:

- **Hojas para estudiar en casa:** Una hoja para estudiar en casa incluye 3 ó 4 tablas de práctica en una página. Su niño puede usar las hojas para practicar todos los conteos, multiplicaciones y divisiones de un número, o para practicar sólo las operaciones para ese número que no domine. El ayudante de tareas usa la hoja para hacerle una prueba (o repetir una prueba) con problemas. Esa persona debe hablar con su niño para decidir sobre qué multiplicaciones o divisiones básicas el niño puede hacer la prueba. La persona que ayude debe marcar ligeramente con un lápiz cualquier problema que conteste mal. Si su niño contesta bien todas las operaciones de una columna, la persona que ayude debe firmar esa columna de la hoja de firmas. Cuando todas las columnas de la hoja de firmas estén firmadas, su niño debe llevar la hoja a la escuela.

Home Study Sheet A

5s			2s		
Count-bys	Mixed Up ×	Mixed Up ÷	Count-bys	Mixed Up ×	Mixed Up ÷
1 × 5 = 5	2 × 5 = 10	10 ÷ 5 = 2	1 × 2 = 2	7 × 2 = 14	20 ÷ 2 = 10
2 × 5 = 10	9 × 5 = 45	35 ÷ 5 = 7	2 × 2 = 4	1 × 2 = 2	2 ÷ 2 = 1
3 × 5 = 15	1 × 5 = 5	50 ÷ 5 = 10	3 × 2 = 6	3 × 2 = 6	6 ÷ 2 = 3
4 × 5 = 20	5 × 5 = 25	5 ÷ 5 = 1	4 × 2 = 8	5 × 2 = 10	16 ÷ 2 = 8
5 × 5 = 25	7 × 5 = 35	20 ÷ 5 = 4	5 × 2 = 10	6 × 2 = 12	12 ÷ 2 = 6
6 × 5 = 30	3 × 5 = 15	15 ÷ 5 = 3	6 × 2 = 12	8 × 2 = 16	4 ÷ 2 = 2
7 × 5 = 35	10 × 5 = 50	30 ÷ 5 = 6	7 × 2 = 14	2 × 2 = 4	10 ÷ 2 = 5
8 × 5 = 40	6 × 5 = 30	40 ÷ 5 = 8	8 × 2 = 16	10 × 2 = 20	8 ÷ 2 = 4
9 × 5 = 45	4 × 5 = 20	25 ÷ 5 = 5	9 × 2 = 18	4 × 2 = 8	14 ÷ 2 = 7
10 × 5 = 50	8 × 5 = 40	45 ÷ 5 = 9	10 × 2 = 20	9 × 2 = 18	18 ÷ 2 = 9

Los niños practican cubriendo las respuestas con su dedo o un lápiz y deslizan su dedo o lápiz hacia abajo para revelar cada respuesta después de decirlo.

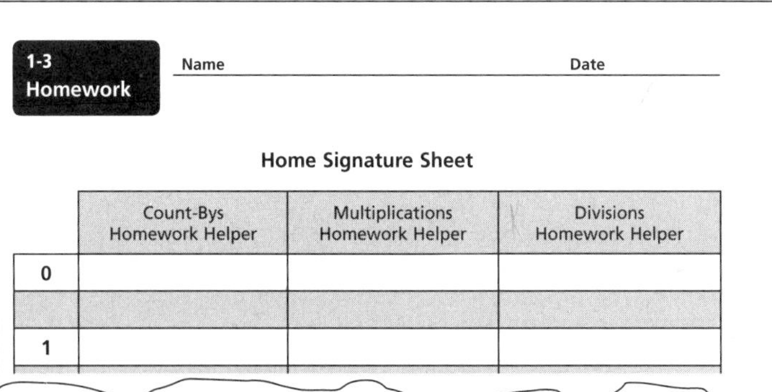

1-3 Homework

Name Date

Home Signature Sheet

	Count-Bys Homework Helper	Multiplications Homework Helper	Divisions Homework Helper
0			
1			

Guarde todos los materiales de práctica en la carpeta que su hijo trajo a casa hoy.

- **Hojas de verificación:** Una hoja de verificación consta de columnas de 20 multiplicaciones y divisiones sin orden fijo. Estas hojas se pueden usar para comprobar el dominio de su niño con las multiplicaciones y divisiones básicas.
- **Tarjetas de estrategias:** Su niño debe usar las Tarjetas de estrategias para practicar la multiplicación y división al responder el problema del frente. Esa tarjeta se pone en una de las tres pilas: *Contesta Rápidamente, Se Demora En Contestar y No Sabe*. Las tarjetas de *Se Demora En Contestar* y *No Sabe* se practican hasta que las contesten rápidamente.

Ejemplo de tarjeta de multiplicación

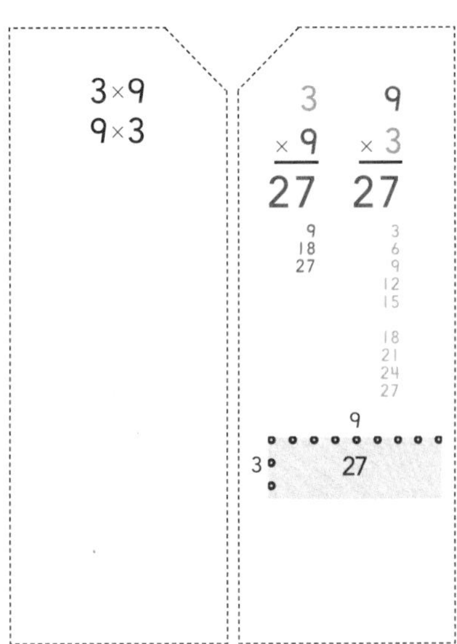

Ejemplo de tarjeta de división

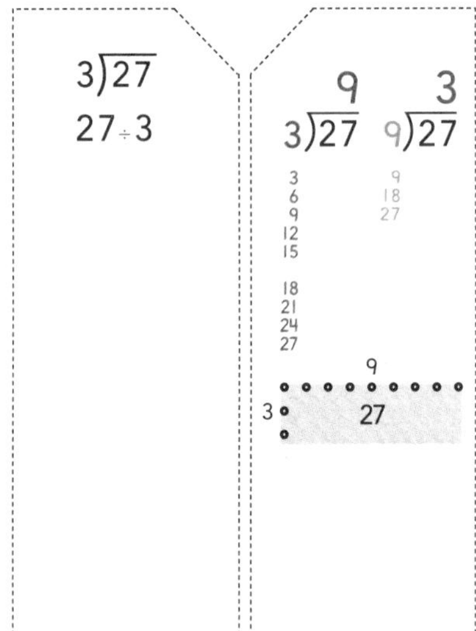

Pida a su niño a que le muestre estos materiales y a que le explique cómo se usan. Su niño debe practicar lo que no sabe todos los días.

Si tiene alguna duda o pregunta, por favor comuníquese conmigo.

Atentamente,
El maestro de su niño

Guarde todos los materiales en la carpeta de práctica en casa.

Name ______________________________

Signature Sheet

	Count-Bys Partner	Multiplications Partner	Divisions Partner	Multiplications Check Sheets	Divisions Check Sheets
5s				1:	1:
2s				1:	1:
10s				2:	2:
9s				2:	2:
				3:	3:
3s				4:	4:
4s				4:	4:
1s				5:	5:
0s				5:	5:
				6:	6:
6s				7:	7:
8s				7:	7:
7s				8:	8:
				9:	9:
				10:	10:

Name

Dash Record Sheet

Dash Number	Accurate	Fast	Really Fast
1			
2			
3			
4			
5			
6			
7			
8			
9			
9A			
9B			
9C			
10			
10A			
10B			
10C			
11			
11A			
11B			
11C			
12			
12A			
12B			
12C			

Dash Number	Accurate	Fast	Really Fast
13			
14			
15			
16			
17			
18			
19			
19A			
19B			
19C			
19D			
20			
20A			
20B			
20C			
20D			
21			
21A			
21B			
21C			
22			
22A			
22B			
22C			

Name ______________________

PATH to FLUENCY

Study Sheet A

5s		
Count-bys	**Mixed Up ×**	**Mixed Up ÷**
1 × 5 = 5	2 × 5 = 10	10 ÷ 5 = 2
2 × 5 = 10	9 × 5 = 45	35 ÷ 5 = 7
3 × 5 = 15	1 × 5 = 5	50 ÷ 5 = 10
4 × 5 = 20	5 × 5 = 25	5 ÷ 5 = 1
5 × 5 = 25	7 × 5 = 35	20 ÷ 5 = 4
6 × 5 = 30	3 × 5 = 15	15 ÷ 5 = 3
7 × 5 = 35	10 × 5 = 50	30 ÷ 5 = 6
8 × 5 = 40	6 × 5 = 30	40 ÷ 5 = 8
9 × 5 = 45	4 × 5 = 20	25 ÷ 5 = 5
10 × 5 = 50	8 × 5 = 40	45 ÷ 5 = 9

2s		
Count-bys	**Mixed Up ×**	**Mixed Up ÷**
1 × 2 = 2	7 × 2 = 14	20 ÷ 2 = 10
2 × 2 = 4	1 × 2 = 2	2 ÷ 2 = 1
3 × 2 = 6	3 × 2 = 6	6 ÷ 2 = 3
4 × 2 = 8	5 × 2 = 10	16 ÷ 2 = 8
5 × 2 = 10	6 × 2 = 12	12 ÷ 2 = 6
6 × 2 = 12	8 × 2 = 16	4 ÷ 2 = 2
7 × 2 = 14	2 × 2 = 4	10 ÷ 2 = 5
8 × 2 = 16	10 × 2 = 20	8 ÷ 2 = 4
9 × 2 = 18	4 × 2 = 8	14 ÷ 2 = 7
10 × 2 = 20	9 × 2 = 18	18 ÷ 2 = 9

10s		
Count-bys	**Mixed Up ×**	**Mixed Up ÷**
1 × 10 = 10	1 × 10 = 10	80 ÷ 10 = 8
2 × 10 = 20	5 × 10 = 50	10 ÷ 10 = 1
3 × 10 = 30	2 × 10 = 20	50 ÷ 10 = 5
4 × 10 = 40	8 × 10 = 80	90 ÷ 10 = 9
5 × 10 = 50	7 × 10 = 70	40 ÷ 10 = 4
6 × 10 = 60	3 × 10 = 30	100 ÷ 10 = 10
7 × 10 = 70	4 × 10 = 40	30 ÷ 10 = 3
8 × 10 = 80	6 × 10 = 60	20 ÷ 10 = 2
9 × 10 = 90	10 × 10 = 100	70 ÷ 10 = 7
10 × 10 = 100	9 × 10 = 90	60 ÷ 10 = 6

9s		
Count-bys	**Mixed Up ×**	**Mixed Up ÷**
1 × 9 = 9	2 × 9 = 18	81 ÷ 9 = 9
2 × 9 = 18	4 × 9 = 36	18 ÷ 9 = 2
3 × 9 = 27	7 × 9 = 63	36 ÷ 9 = 4
4 × 9 = 36	8 × 9 = 72	9 ÷ 9 = 1
5 × 9 = 45	3 × 9 = 27	54 ÷ 9 = 6
6 × 9 = 54	10 × 9 = 90	27 ÷ 9 = 3
7 × 9 = 63	1 × 9 = 9	63 ÷ 9 = 7
8 × 9 = 72	6 × 9 = 54	72 ÷ 9 = 8
9 × 9 = 81	5 × 9 = 45	90 ÷ 9 = 10
10 × 9 = 90	9 × 9 = 81	45 ÷ 9 = 5

Name ____________________

Explore Arrays

VOCABULARY
array column
row

An **array** is an arrangement of objects in **rows** and **columns**. You can use multiplication to find the total number of objects in an array.

2 rows of 5 = 2 × 5 = 10

2-by-5 array
5 columns

2 rows

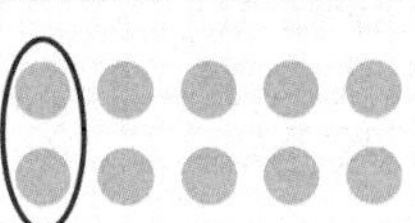

PATH to FLUENCY Write Multiplication Equations

Write a multiplication equation for each array.

1. How many flowers?

____

2. How many shells?

____

3. How many mugs?

____

4. **Math Journal** Write a problem that you can solve by using this array. Show how to solve your problem.

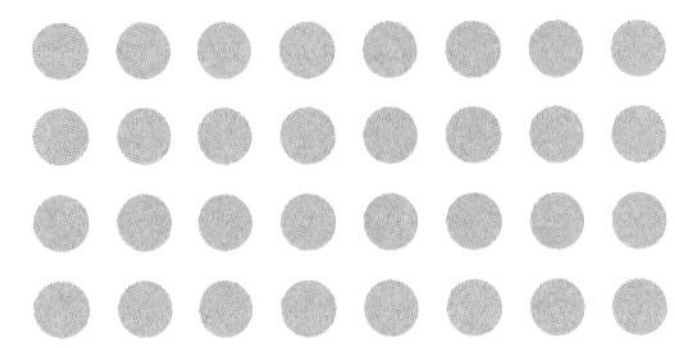

Compare Arrays

VOCABULARY
(>) is greater than
(<) is less than

Without counting the dots in the array, write $>$, $<$, or $=$ in the circle.

5 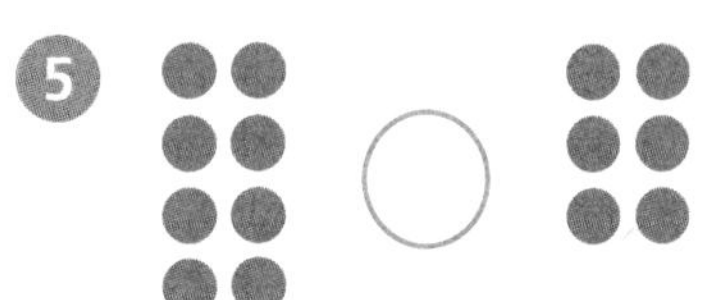

6 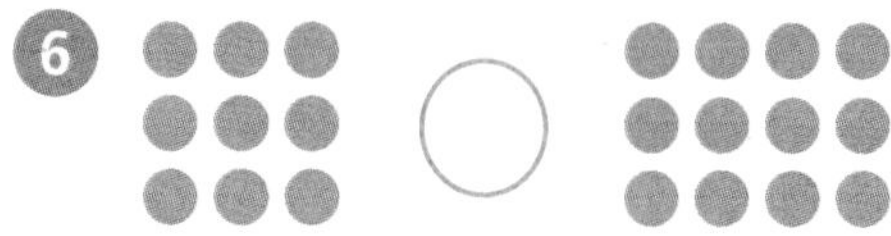

7 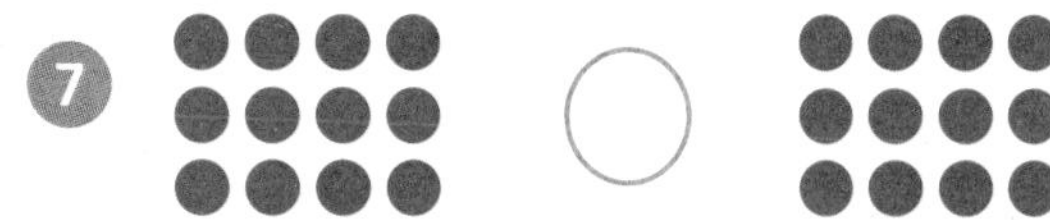

8 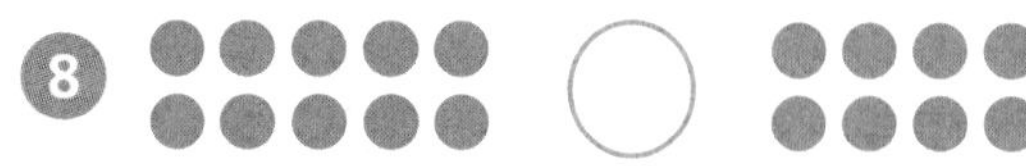

9 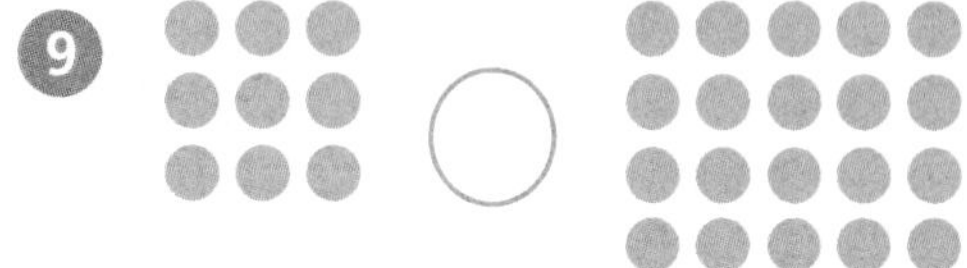

10 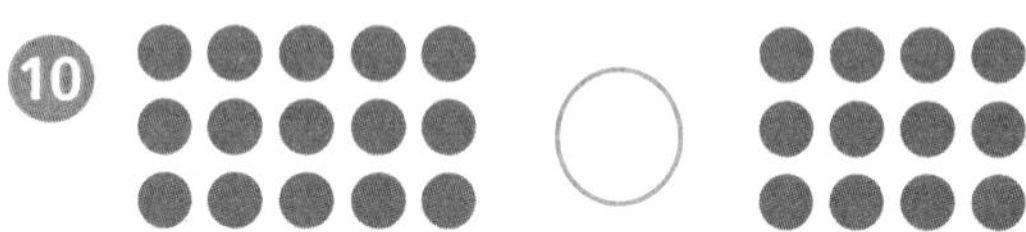

11 

12 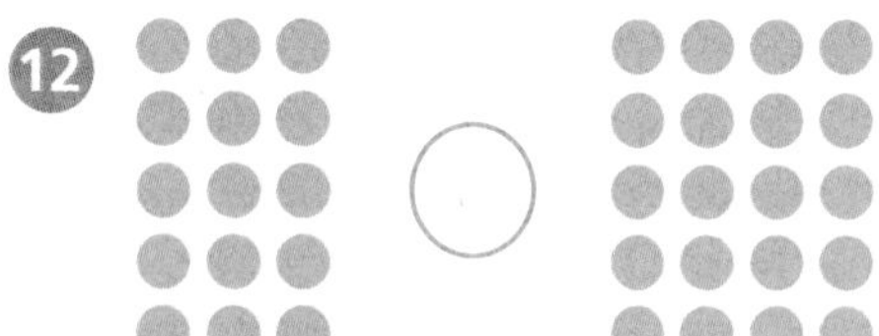

13 **Create Your Own** Draw two dot arrays and compare them using symbols. Then write an equation for each array to show that your comparison is correct.

Name ______________________

What's the Error?

Dear Math Students,

Today I found the unknown number in this division equation by using a related multiplication. Is my calculation correct?

$40 \div 5 = \square$ $\qquad$ $\boxed{9} \times 5 = 40$

If not, please correct my work and tell me what I did wrong. How do you know my answer is wrong?

Your friend,
Puzzled Penguin

5 Write a response to Puzzled Penguin.

___

___

___

___

___

PATH to FLUENCY Relate Division and Multiplication Equations with 5

Find the unknown numbers.

6 $20 \div (5) = \square$ $\qquad$ $\square \times (5) = 20$

$20 \div (4) = \square$ $\qquad$ $\square \times (4) = 20$

7 $10 \div (5) = \square$ $\qquad$ $\square \times (5) = 10$

$10 \div (2) = \square$ $\qquad$ $\square \times (2) = 10$

8 $15 \div (5) = \square$ $\qquad$ $\square \times (5) = 15$

$15 \div (3) = \square$ $\qquad$ $\square \times (3) = 15$

Find the Number in Each Group

Write an equation and solve the problem.

Show your work.

9 Aziz put 15 ice cubes in 5 glasses. He put the same number of ice cubes in each glass. How many ice cubes did he put in each glass?

____

10 Lori's uncle gave her 20 stickers. She put the same number of stickers on each of 5 folders. How many stickers did she put on each folder?

____

11 Todd cut a board that measured 45 inches in length into 5 pieces. Each piece he cut measures the same number of inches. How many inches does each piece measure?

____

12 Ten students gathered into 5 groups to play a math game. The same number of students are in each group. How many students are in each group?

____

Check Understanding

What multiplication equation with an unknown number can you write to find $20 \div 5 = \square$?

____

Solve the equation to find the unknown number. $\square$

Name ______________________________

PATH to FLUENCY

Explore Patterns with 2s

What patterns do you see below?

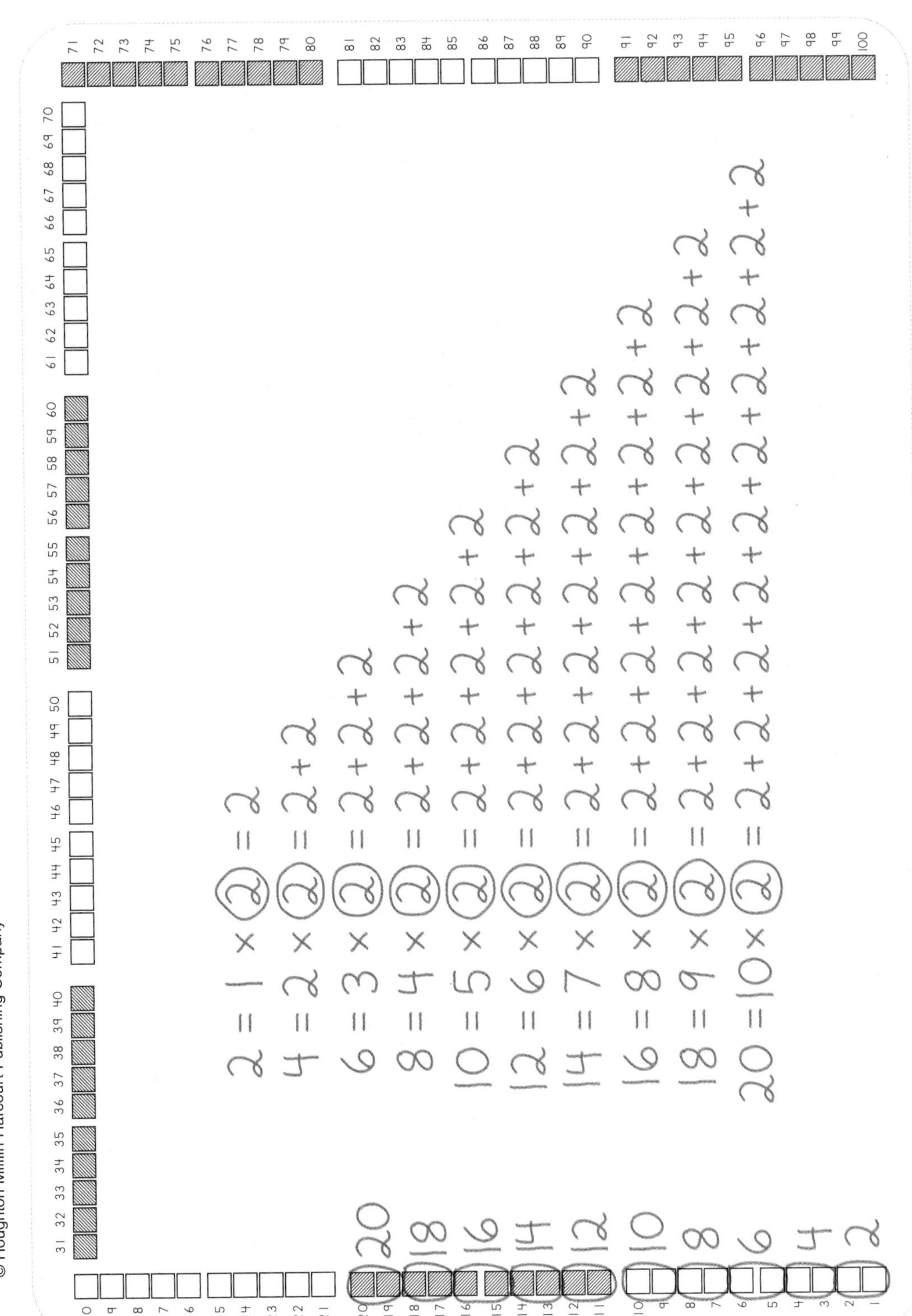

Even and Odd Numbers

VOCABULARY
even number
odd number
pictograph

The 2s count-bys are called *even numbers* because they are multiples of 2. In an **even number**, the ones digit is 0, 2, 4, 6, or 8. If a number is not a multiple of two, it is called an **odd number**.

Tell whether each number is even or odd.

1. 7 ______
2. 4 ______
3. 20 ______
4. 15 ______

Solve Multiplication and Division Problems with 2s

Write an equation and solve the problem.

5. At the art fair, Tamika sold 9 pairs of earrings. How many individual earrings did she sell?

______

6. Rhonda divided 8 crayons equally between her twin brothers. How many crayons did each boy get?

______

Use the pictograph to solve each problem.

7. In all, how many Strawberry Sensation and Citrus Surprise drinks were sold?

______

8. How many more Peach-Banana Blast drinks were sold than Mango Madness drinks?

______

Drinks Sold at the Smoothie Shop	
Strawberry Sensation	🥤🥤🥤
Peach-Banana Blast	🥤🥤🥤🥤🥤🥤🥤 and a half cup
Mango Madness	🥤🥤
Citrus Surprise	🥤🥤🥤🥤🥤
Each 🥤 stands for 2 drinks.	

Check Understanding

Explain how patterns in the 2s count-bys and multiplications can help you when multiplying.

Name ____________________

PATH to FLUENCY

Check Sheet 1: 5s and 2s

5s Multiplications	5s Divisions	2s Multiplications	2s Divisions
2 × 5 = 10	30 / 5 = 6	4 × 2 = 8	8 / 2 = 4
5 • 6 = 30	5 ÷ 5 = 1	2 • 8 = 16	18 ÷ 2 = 9
5 * 9 = 45	15 / 5 = 3	1 * 2 = 2	2 / 2 = 1
4 × 5 = 20	50 ÷ 5 = 10	6 × 2 = 12	16 ÷ 2 = 8
5 • 7 = 35	20 / 5 = 4	2 • 9 = 18	4 / 2 = 2
10 * 5 = 50	10 ÷ 5 = 2	2 * 2 = 4	20 ÷ 2 = 10
1 × 5 = 5	35 / 5 = 7	3 × 2 = 6	10 / 2 = 5
5 • 3 = 15	40 ÷ 5 = 8	2 • 5 = 10	12 ÷ 2 = 6
8 * 5 = 40	25 / 5 = 5	10 * 2 = 20	6 / 2 = 3
5 × 5 = 25	45 / 5 = 9	2 × 7 = 14	14 / 2 = 7
5 • 8 = 40	20 ÷ 5 = 4	2 • 10 = 20	4 ÷ 2 = 2
7 * 5 = 35	15 / 5 = 3	9 * 2 = 18	2 / 2 = 1
5 × 4 = 20	30 ÷ 5 = 6	2 × 6 = 12	8 ÷ 2 = 4
6 • 5 = 30	25 / 5 = 5	8 • 2 = 16	6 / 2 = 3
5 * 1 = 5	10 ÷ 5 = 2	2 * 3 = 6	20 ÷ 2 = 10
5 × 10 = 50	45 / 5 = 9	2 × 2 = 4	14 / 2 = 7
9 • 5 = 45	35 ÷ 5 = 7	1 • 2 = 2	10 ÷ 2 = 5
5 * 2 = 10	50 ÷ 5 = 10	2 * 4 = 8	16 ÷ 2 = 8
3 × 5 = 15	40 / 5 = 8	5 × 2 = 10	12 / 2 = 6
5 • 5 = 25	5 ÷ 5 = 1	7 • 2 = 14	18 ÷ 2 = 9

Name ________________________

PATH to FLUENCY Use the Target

×	0	1	2	3	4	5	6	7	8	9
0	0	0	0	0	0	0	0	0	0	0
1	0	1	2	3	4	5	6	7	8	9
2	0	2	4	6	8	10	12	14	16	18
3	0	3	6	9	12	15	18	21	24	27
4	0	4	8	12	16	20	24	28	32	36
5	0	5	10	15	20	25	30	35	40	45
6	0	6	12	18	24	30	36	42	48	54
7	0	7	14	21	28	35	42	49	56	63
8	0	8	16	24	32	40	48	56	64	72
9	0	9	18	27	36	45	54	63	72	81

1. Discuss how you can use the Target to find the product for 8×5.
2. Discuss how you can use the Target to practice division.
3. Practice using the Target.
4. When using the Target, how are multiplication and division alike? How are they different?

____

____

____

____

____

____

____

Make Sense of Problems

Write an equation and solve the problem.

Show your work.

5 Mrs. Cheng bought 8 pairs of mittens. How many individual mittens did she buy?

____

6 Brian divided 10 crayons equally between his two sisters. How many crayons did each girl get?

____

7 Maria has 5 piles of flash cards. There are 9 cards in each pile. How many flash cards does Maria have?

____

8 A parking lot has 5 rows of parking spaces with the same number of spaces in each row. There are 35 parking spaces in the lot. How many spaces are in each row?

____

Write a Word Problem

9 Write a word problem that can be solved using the equation $45 \div 5 = \square$, where 5 is the number of groups.

____

____

____

____

Check Understanding

If you know that $7 \times 2 = 14$, what other multiplications and divisions do you know?

____

Name ______________________ Date ______________

Write the correct answer.

1. $5 \times 3 = \square$

2. $18 \div 2 = \square$

3. Complete the multiplication sentence.

   $5 \times 6 = 6 \times \square$

4. Andy uses 3 bananas in each of 5 loaves of banana bread he is baking. Write a multiplication expression to represent the total number of bananas Andy uses.

   Show your work.

   ____

5. Solve to find the unknown number in the equation.

   $5 \times \square = 40$

Strategy Check 1

Name ______________________ Date ______________________

Make a drawing. Write an equation. Solve.

1. Imaad has 5 bowls. He wants to serve 4 dumplings in each bowl. How many dumplings does he need in all?

____

2. Marja arranges her toy cars so 7 toy cars are in each row. She makes 3 equal rows of toy cars. How many toy cars does Marja have?

____

3. Noriko pastes stars on the first page of her book. She arranges the stars in 2 rows with 4 stars in each row. On the second page, she pastes 2 stars in a row. There are 4 rows of stars on the second page. How many stars are on each page?

____

Name ______________________

PATH to FLUENCY

Explore Patterns with 10s

What patterns do you see below?

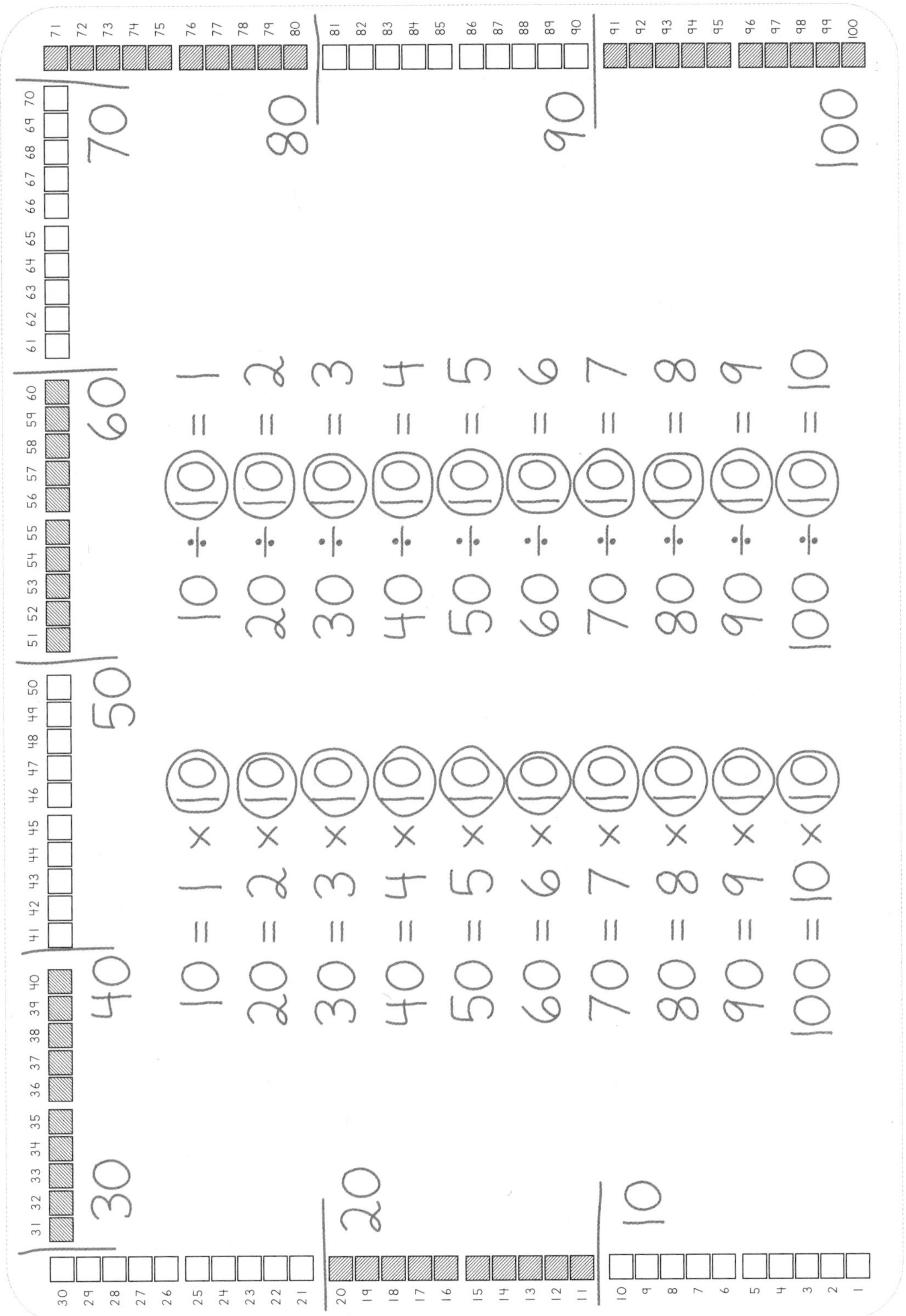

$10 = 1 \times 10$
$20 = 2 \times 10$
$30 = 3 \times 10$
$40 = 4 \times 10$
$50 = 5 \times 10$
$60 = 6 \times 10$
$70 = 7 \times 10$
$80 = 8 \times 10$
$90 = 9 \times 10$
$100 = 10 \times 10$

$10 \div 10 = 1$
$20 \div 10 = 2$
$30 \div 10 = 3$
$40 \div 10 = 4$
$50 \div 10 = 5$
$60 \div 10 = 6$
$70 \div 10 = 7$
$80 \div 10 = 8$
$90 \div 10 = 9$
$100 \div 10 = 10$

10 20 30 40 50 60 70 80 90 100

Solve Problems with 10s

Write an equation and solve the problem.

Show your work.

1. Raymundo has 9 dimes. How many cents does he have?

___

2. Yoko has some dimes in her pocket, and no other coins. She has a total of 70¢. How many dimes does she have?

___

3. Jonah picked 40 strawberries. He gave them to 10 of his friends. Each friend got the same number of strawberries. How many strawberries did each friend get?

___

4. There are 10 Space Command trading cards in each pack. Zoe bought 5 packs of cards. How many cards did she buy in all?

___

5. There were 80 students in the auditorium. There were 10 students in each row. How many rows of students were there?

___

6. A roll of ribbon has 60 inches of ribbon. Harper cut all the ribbon into 10 equal length pieces. How many inches long is each piece?

___

Name ______________________

Use Variables in Equations

VOCABULARY
variable

When you write equations you can use a letter to represent an unknown number. This letter is called a **variable**.

Each of these equations has a variable.

$a \times 10 = 60$ $\quad 70 = c \times 7$ $\quad w = 80 \div 10$ $\quad 9 = 90 \div c$

$2 \times y = 18$ $\quad p = 9 \times 2$ $\quad f = 18 \div 2$ $\quad 18 \div n = 2$

Solve each equation.

7. $14 = 7 \times a$

   $a =$ ____

8. $90 \div g = 9$

   $g =$ ____

9. $10 \div n = 5$

   $n =$ ____

10. $8 \times f = 40$

    $f =$ ____

Write and Solve Equations with Variables

Write an equation and solve the problem.

11. A box of straws holds 60 straws. There are 10 straws in each row. How many rows are there?

    ____

12. Ethan used 9 dimes to pay for his book. How much did his book cost?

    ____

13. There are 10 relay teams with an equal number of people on each team running a race. There are 50 people running the race. How many people are there on each team?

    ____

14. Amanda has 20 bracelets. She gave the same number of bracelets to 2 of her friends. How many bracelets did she give to each friend?

    ____

What's the Error?

Dear Math Students,

Today my teacher asked me to write a word problem that can be solved using the division $40 \div 10$. Here is the problem I wrote:

> Kim has 40 apples and puts 4 apples in each bag. How many bags does Kim use?

Is my problem correct? If not, please correct my work and tell me what I did wrong.

Your friend,
Puzzled Penguin

15 **Write an answer to the Puzzled Penguin.**

Write and Solve Problems with 10s

16 Write a word problem that can be solved using the multiplication 10×3. Then write a related division word problem.

Check Understanding

Give an example of a number that is a 10s count-by and explain how you know.

Name ____________________

PATH to FLUENCY

Check Sheet 2: 10s and 9s

10s Multiplications	10s Divisions	9s Multiplications	9s Divisions
9 × 10 = 90	100 / 10 = 10	3 × 9 = 27	27 / 9 = 3
10 • 3 = 30	50 ÷ 10 = 5	9 • 7 = 63	9 ÷ 9 = 1
10 * 6 = 60	70 / 10 = 7	10 * 9 = 90	81 / 9 = 9
1 × 10 = 10	40 ÷ 10 = 4	5 × 9 = 45	45 ÷ 9 = 5
10 • 4 = 40	80 / 10 = 8	9 • 8 = 72	90 / 9 = 10
10 * 7 = 70	60 ÷ 10 = 6	9 * 1 = 9	36 ÷ 9 = 4
8 × 10 = 80	10 / 10 = 1	2 × 9 = 18	18 / 9 = 2
10 • 10 = 100	20 ÷ 10 = 2	9 • 9 = 81	63 ÷ 9 = 7
5 * 10 = 50	90 / 10 = 9	6 * 9 = 54	54 / 9 = 6
10 × 2 = 20	30 / 10 = 3	9 × 4 = 36	72 / 9 = 8
10 • 5 = 50	80 ÷ 10 = 8	9 • 5 = 45	27 ÷ 9 = 3
4 * 10 = 40	70 / 10 = 7	4 * 9 = 36	45 / 9 = 5
10 × 1 = 10	100 ÷ 10 = 10	9 × 1 = 9	63 ÷ 9 = 7
3 • 10 = 30	90 / 10 = 9	3 • 9 = 27	72 / 9 = 8
10 * 8 = 80	60 ÷ 10 = 6	9 * 8 = 72	54 ÷ 9 = 6
7 × 10 = 70	30 / 10 = 3	7 × 9 = 63	18 / 9 = 2
6 • 10 = 60	10 ÷ 10 = 1	6 • 9 = 54	90 ÷ 9 = 10
10 * 9 = 90	40 ÷ 10 = 4	9 * 9 = 81	9 ÷ 9 = 1
10 × 10 = 100	20 / 10 = 2	10 × 9 = 90	36 / 9 = 4
2 • 10 = 20	50 ÷ 10 = 5	2 • 9 = 18	81 ÷ 9 = 9

Name ________________________________

Math Tools: Quick 9s Multiplication

You can use the Quick 9s method to help you multiply by 9. Open your hands and turn them so they are facing you. Imagine that your fingers are numbered like this.

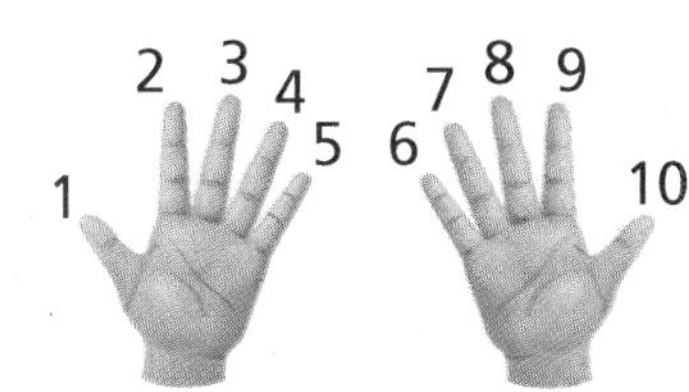

To find a number times 9, bend down the finger for that number. For example, to find 4 × 9, bend down your fourth finger.

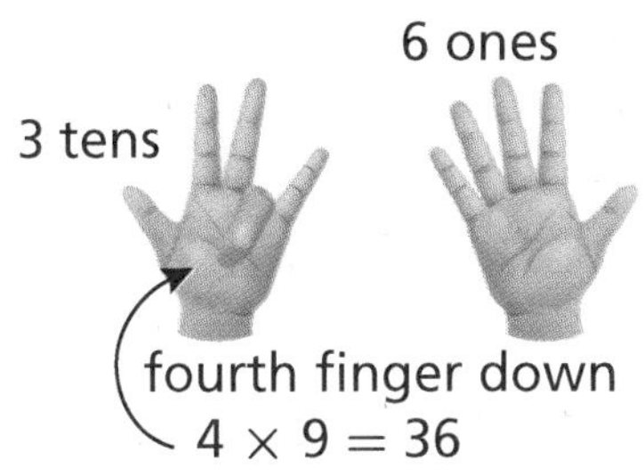

The fingers to the left of your bent finger are the tens. The fingers to the right are the ones. For this problem, there are 3 tens and 6 ones, so 4 × 9 = 36.

Why does this work? Because 4 × 9 = 4 × (10 − 1) = 40 − 4 = 36

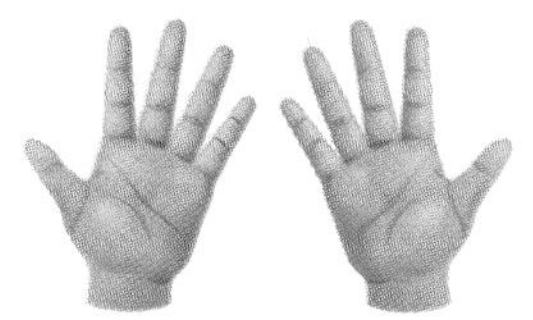
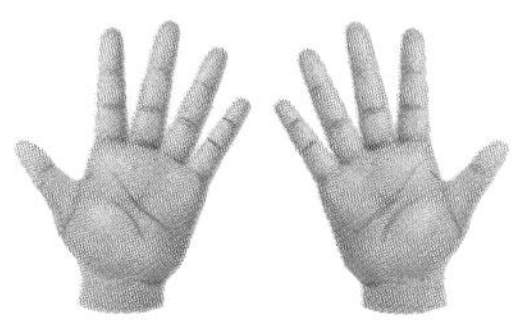
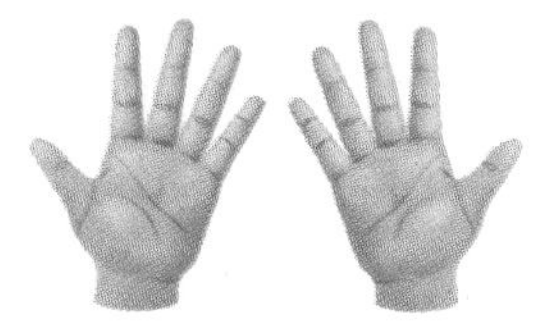
+
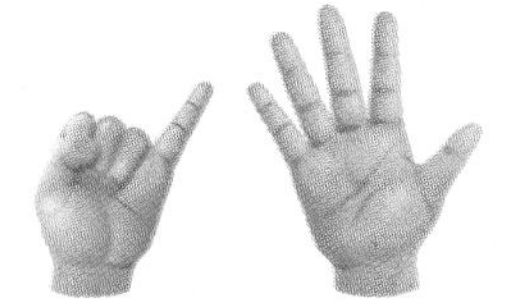

3 tens   6 ones

1 Write the multiplication that is shown when the seventh multiplier finger is down.

____ × ____ = ____

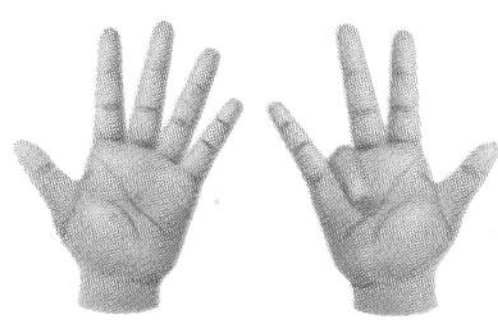

2 Which multiplier finger will be down to show 5 tens and 4 ones?

____

Math Tools: Quick 9s Division

You can also use Quick 9s to help you divide by 9.
For example, to find 72 ÷ 9, show 72 on your fingers.

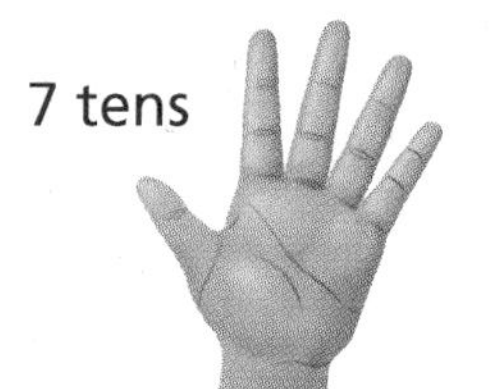

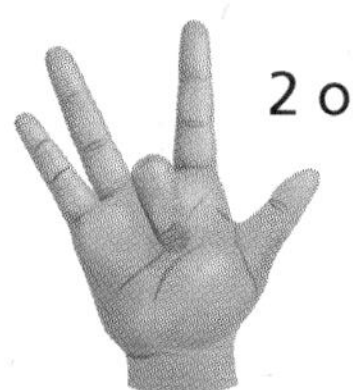

Your eighth finger is down, so $72 \div 9 = 8$.
$8 \times 9 = 80 - 8 = 72$

3. Write the division that is shown when the fifth multiplier finger is down.

   _____ ÷ _____ = _____

4. Which multiplier finger will be down to show $81 \div 9$?

   ____

5. Which multiplication is shown when the ninth finger is down?

   _____ × _____ = _____

Check Understanding

Use the picture below. Draw an X on the finger that you would bend down to find 6×9.

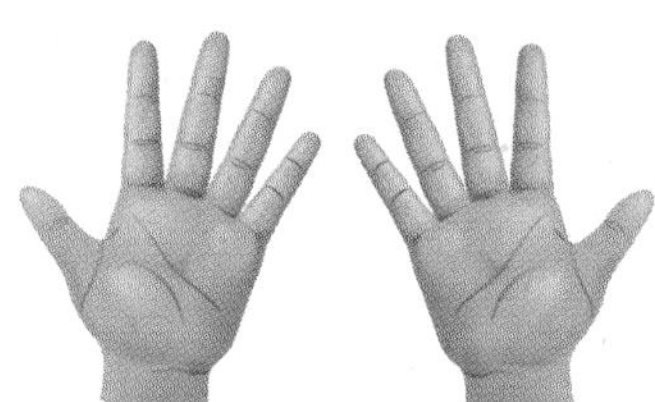

$6 \times 9 = \square$

Use the picture below. Draw an X on the finger that you would bend down to find $27 \div 9$.

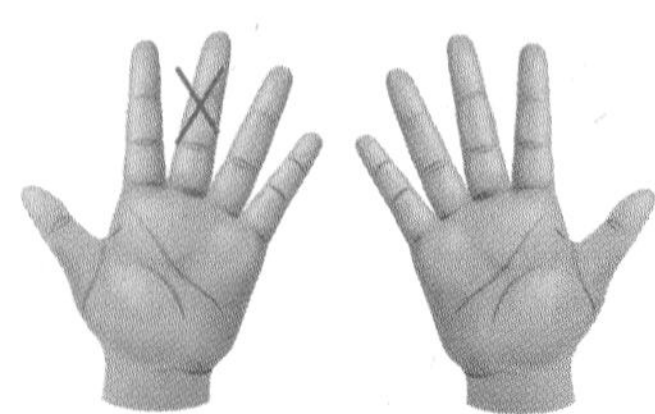

$27 \div 9 = \square$

Name ______________________________

PATH to FLUENCY **Check Sheet 3: 2s, 5s, 9s, and 10s**

2s, 5s, 9s, 10s Multiplications	2s, 5s, 9s, 10s Multiplications	2s, 5s, 9s, 10s Divisions	2s, 5s, 9s, 10s Divisions
2 × 10 = 20	5 × 10 = 50	18 / 2 = 9	36 / 9 = 4
10 • 5 = 50	10 • 9 = 90	50 ÷ 5 = 10	70 ÷ 10 = 7
9 * 6 = 54	4 * 10 = 40	72 / 9 = 8	18 / 2 = 9
7 × 10 = 70	2 × 9 = 18	60 ÷ 10 = 6	45 ÷ 5 = 9
2 • 3 = 6	5 • 3 = 15	12 / 2 = 6	45 / 9 = 5
5 * 7 = 35	6 * 9 = 54	30 ÷ 5 = 6	30 ÷ 10 = 3
9 × 10 = 90	10 × 3 = 30	18 / 9 = 2	6 / 2 = 3
6 • 10 = 60	3 • 2 = 6	50 ÷ 10 = 5	50 ÷ 5 = 10
8 * 2 = 16	5 * 8 = 40	14 / 2 = 7	27 / 9 = 3
5 × 6 = 30	9 × 9 = 81	25 / 5 = 5	70 / 10 = 7
9 • 5 = 45	10 • 4 = 40	81 ÷ 9 = 9	20 ÷ 2 = 10
8 * 10 = 80	9 * 2 = 18	20 / 10 = 2	45 / 5 = 9
2 × 1 = 2	5 × 1 = 5	8 ÷ 2 = 4	54 ÷ 9 = 6
3 • 5 = 15	9 • 6 = 54	45 / 5 = 9	80 / 10 = 8
4 * 9 = 36	10 * 1 = 10	63 ÷ 9 = 7	16 ÷ 2 = 8
3 × 10 = 30	7 × 2 = 14	30 / 10 = 3	15 / 5 = 3
2 • 6 = 12	6 • 5 = 30	10 ÷ 2 = 5	90 ÷ 9 = 10
4 * 5 = 20	8 * 9 = 72	40 ÷ 5 = 8	100 ÷ 10 = 10
9 × 7 = 63	10 × 6 = 60	9 / 9 = 1	12 / 2 = 6
1 • 10 = 10	2 • 8 = 16	50 ÷ 10 = 5	35 ÷ 5 = 7

Name

PATH to FLUENCY

Study Sheet B

3s		
Count-bys	**Mixed Up ×**	**Mixed Up ÷**
1 × 3 = 3	5 × 3 = 15	27 ÷ 3 = 9
2 × 3 = 6	1 × 3 = 3	6 ÷ 3 = 2
3 × 3 = 9	8 × 3 = 24	18 ÷ 3 = 6
4 × 3 = 12	10 × 3 = 30	30 ÷ 3 = 10
5 × 3 = 15	3 × 3 = 9	9 ÷ 3 = 3
6 × 3 = 18	7 × 3 = 21	3 ÷ 3 = 1
7 × 3 = 21	9 × 3 = 27	12 ÷ 3 = 4
8 × 3 = 24	2 × 3 = 6	24 ÷ 3 = 8
9 × 3 = 27	4 × 3 = 12	15 ÷ 3 = 5
10 × 3 = 30	6 × 3 = 18	21 ÷ 3 = 7

4s		
Count-bys	**Mixed Up ×**	**Mixed Up ÷**
1 × 4 = 4	4 × 4 = 16	12 ÷ 4 = 3
2 × 4 = 8	1 × 4 = 4	36 ÷ 4 = 9
3 × 4 = 12	7 × 4 = 28	24 ÷ 4 = 6
4 × 4 = 16	3 × 4 = 12	4 ÷ 4 = 1
5 × 4 = 20	9 × 4 = 36	20 ÷ 4 = 5
6 × 4 = 24	10 × 4 = 40	28 ÷ 4 = 7
7 × 4 = 28	2 × 4 = 8	8 ÷ 4 = 2
8 × 4 = 32	5 × 4 = 20	40 ÷ 4 = 10
9 × 4 = 36	8 × 4 = 32	32 ÷ 4 = 8
10 × 4 = 40	6 × 4 = 24	16 ÷ 4 = 4

0s	
Count-bys	**Mixed Up ×**
1 × 0 = 0	3 × 0 = 0
2 × 0 = 0	10 × 0 = 0
3 × 0 = 0	5 × 0 = 0
4 × 0 = 0	8 × 0 = 0
5 × 0 = 0	7 × 0 = 0
6 × 0 = 0	2 × 0 = 0
7 × 0 = 0	9 × 0 = 0
8 × 0 = 0	6 × 0 = 0
9 × 0 = 0	1 × 0 = 0
10 × 0 = 0	4 × 0 = 0

1s		
Count-bys	**Mixed Up ×**	**Mixed Up ÷**
1 × 1 = 1	5 × 1 = 5	10 ÷ 1 = 10
2 × 1 = 2	7 × 1 = 7	8 ÷ 1 = 8
3 × 1 = 3	10 × 1 = 10	4 ÷ 1 = 4
4 × 1 = 4	1 × 1 = 1	9 ÷ 1 = 9
5 × 1 = 5	8 × 1 = 8	6 ÷ 1 = 6
6 × 1 = 6	4 × 1 = 4	7 ÷ 1 = 7
7 × 1 = 7	9 × 1 = 9	1 ÷ 1 = 1
8 × 1 = 8	3 × 1 = 3	2 ÷ 1 = 2
9 × 1 = 9	2 × 1 = 2	5 ÷ 1 = 5
10 × 1 = 10	6 × 1 = 6	3 ÷ 1 = 3

2×2	$\begin{array}{r} 2 \\ \times\ 3 \\ \hline \end{array}$ $\begin{array}{r} 3 \\ \times\ 2 \\ \hline \end{array}$	2×4 4×2	$\begin{array}{r} 2 \\ \times\ 5 \\ \hline \end{array}$ $\begin{array}{r} 5 \\ \times\ 2 \\ \hline \end{array}$
2×6 6×2	$\begin{array}{r} 2 \\ \times\ 7 \\ \hline \end{array}$ $\begin{array}{r} 7 \\ \times\ 2 \\ \hline \end{array}$	2×8 8×2	$\begin{array}{r} 2 \\ \times\ 9 \\ \hline \end{array}$ $\begin{array}{r} 9 \\ \times\ 2 \\ \hline \end{array}$

$10 = 2 \times 5$

$10 = 5 \times 2$

5 10

2 4 6 8 10

5

2 10

$$\begin{array}{r} 2 \\ \times 4 \\ \hline 8 \end{array} \qquad \begin{array}{r} 4 \\ \times 2 \\ \hline 8 \end{array}$$

2 4 6 8

4 8

2

4 8

$6 = 2 \times 3$

$6 = 3 \times 2$

3 6

2 4 6

3

2 6

$$\begin{array}{r} 2 \\ \times 2 \\ \hline 4 \end{array}$$

2 4

2

2 4

$18 = 2 \times 9$

$18 = 9 \times 2$

9 18

2 4 6 8 10 12 14 16 18

9

2 18

$$\begin{array}{r} 2 \\ \times 8 \\ \hline 16 \end{array} \qquad \begin{array}{r} 8 \\ \times 2 \\ \hline 16 \end{array}$$

8 16

2 4 6 8 10 12 14 16

2

8 16

$14 = 2 \times 7$

$14 = 7 \times 2$

7 14

2 4 6 8 10 12 14

7

2 14

$$\begin{array}{r} 2 \\ \times 6 \\ \hline 12 \end{array} \qquad \begin{array}{r} 6 \\ \times 2 \\ \hline 12 \end{array}$$

6 12

2 4 6 8 10 12

2

6 12

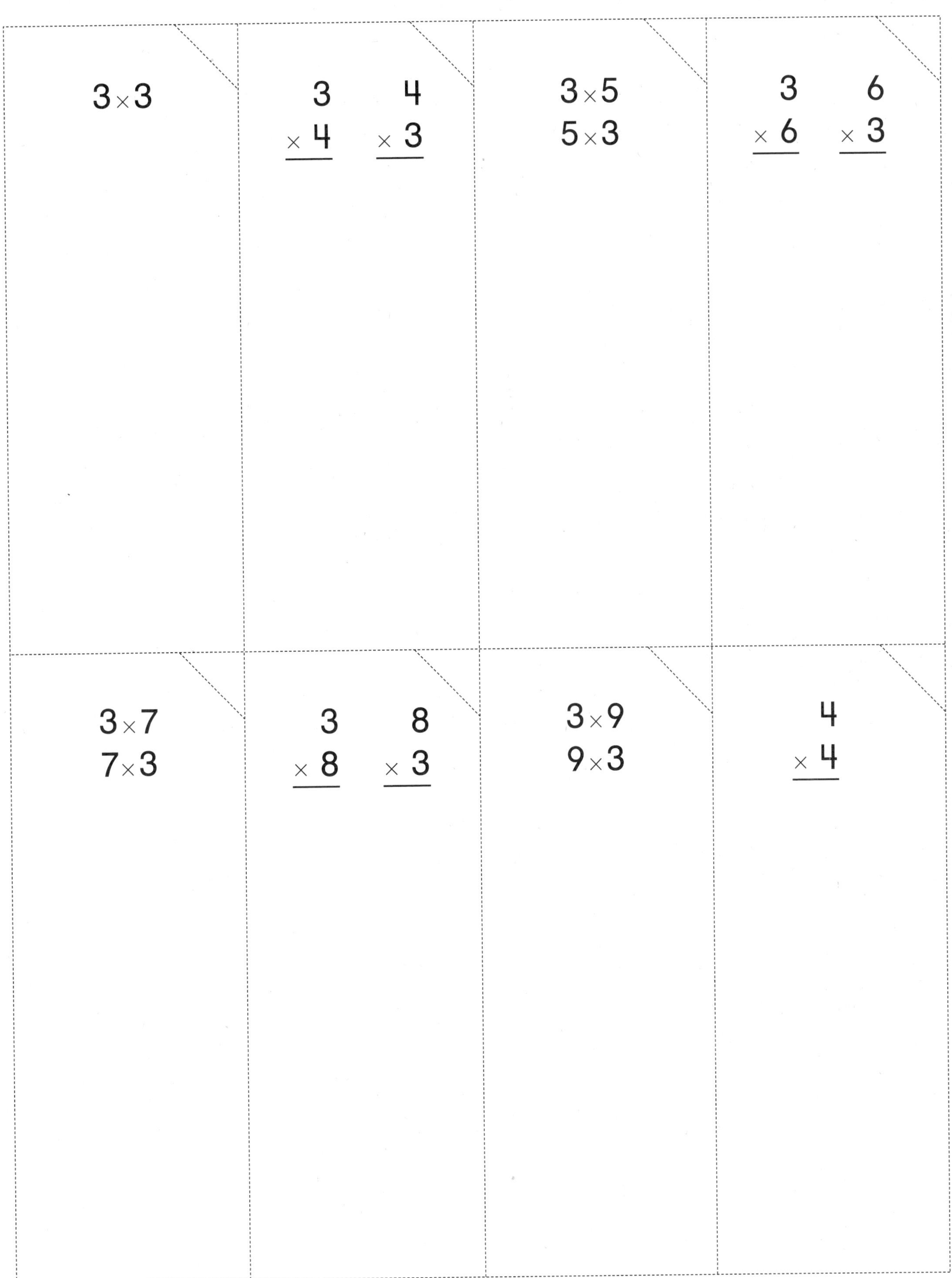

3 × 3
3 × 4
4 × 3
3 × 5
5 × 3
3 × 6
6 × 3
3 × 7
7 × 3
3 × 8
8 × 3
3 × 9
9 × 3
4 × 4

$18 = 3 \times 6$

$18 = 6 \times 3$

6, 12, 18 | 3, 6, 9, 12, 15, 18

6
3 18

$3 \times 5 = 15$ | $5 \times 3 = 15$

5, 10, 15 | 3, 6, 9, 12, 15

3
5 15

$12 = 3 \times 4$

$12 = 4 \times 3$

4, 8, 12 | 3, 6, 9, 12

4
3 12

$3 \times 3 = 9$

3, 6, 9

3
3 9

$16 = 4 \times 4$

4, 8, 12, 16

4
4 16

$3 \times 9 = 27$ | $9 \times 3 = 27$

9, 18, 27 | 3, 6, 9, 12, 15, 18, 21, 24, 27

9
3 27

$24 = 3 \times 8$

$24 = 8 \times 3$

8, 16, 24 | 3, 6, 9, 12, 15, 18, 21, 24

3
8 24

$3 \times 7 = 21$ | $7 \times 3 = 21$

7, 14, 21 | 3, 6, 9, 12, 15, 18, 21

7
3 21

4×5 5×4	$\begin{array}{r} 4 \\ \times\ 6 \\ \hline \end{array}$ $\begin{array}{r} 6 \\ \times\ 4 \\ \hline \end{array}$	4×7 7×4	$\begin{array}{r} 4 \\ \times\ 8 \\ \hline \end{array}$ $\begin{array}{r} 8 \\ \times\ 4 \\ \hline \end{array}$
4×9 9×4	$\begin{array}{r} 5 \\ \times\ 5 \\ \hline \end{array}$	5×6 6×5	$\begin{array}{r} 5 \\ \times\ 7 \\ \hline \end{array}$ $\begin{array}{r} 7 \\ \times\ 5 \\ \hline \end{array}$

32 = 4 × 8

32 = 8 × 4

8 16 24 32

4 8 12 16 20 24 28 32

4

8

32

$$\begin{array}{r} 4 \\ \times 7 \\ \hline 28 \end{array} \qquad \begin{array}{r} 7 \\ \times 4 \\ \hline 28 \end{array}$$

7 14 21 28

4 8 12 16 20 24 28

7

4

28

---

24 = 4 × 6

24 = 6 × 4

6 12 18 24

4 8 12 16 20 24

4

6

24

$$\begin{array}{r} 4 \\ \times 5 \\ \hline 20 \end{array} \qquad \begin{array}{r} 5 \\ \times 4 \\ \hline 20 \end{array}$$

5 10 15 20

4 8 12 16 20

5

4

20

---

35 = 5 × 7

35 = 7 × 5

7 14 21 28 35

5 10 15 20 25 30 35

7

5

35

$$\begin{array}{r} 5 \\ \times 6 \\ \hline 30 \end{array} \qquad \begin{array}{r} 6 \\ \times 5 \\ \hline 30 \end{array}$$

6 12 18 24 30

5 10 15 20 25 30

5

6

30

---

25 = 5 × 5

5 10 15 20 25

5

5

25

$$\begin{array}{r} 4 \\ \times 9 \\ \hline 36 \end{array} \qquad \begin{array}{r} 9 \\ \times 4 \\ \hline 36 \end{array}$$

9 18 27 36

4 8 12 16 20 24 28 32 36

9

4

36

5×8
8×5

$\begin{array}{r} 5 \\ \times\ 9 \\ \hline \end{array}$ $\begin{array}{r} 9 \\ \times\ 5 \\ \hline \end{array}$

6×6

$\begin{array}{r} 6 \\ \times\ 7 \\ \hline \end{array}$ $\begin{array}{r} 7 \\ \times\ 6 \\ \hline \end{array}$

6×8
8×6

$\begin{array}{r} 6 \\ \times\ 9 \\ \hline \end{array}$ $\begin{array}{r} 9 \\ \times\ 6 \\ \hline \end{array}$

7×7

$\begin{array}{r} 7 \\ \times\ 8 \\ \hline \end{array}$ $\begin{array}{r} 8 \\ \times\ 7 \\ \hline \end{array}$

42 = 7 × 6

42 = 6 × 7

6 12 18 24 30 36 42

7 14 21 28 35 42

7

6

42

6

× 6

36

6 12 18 24 30 36

6

6

36

45 = 9 × 5

45 = 5 × 9

5 10 15 20 25 30 35 40 45

9 18 27 36 45

9

5

45

8 × 5 = 40

5 × 8 = 40

5 10 15 20 25 30 35 40

8 16 24 32 40

5

8

40

56 = 7 × 8

56 = 8 × 7

8 16 24 32 40 48 56

7 14 21 28 35 42 49 56

8

7

56

7

× 7

49

7 14 21 28 35 42 49

7

7

49

54 = 9 × 6

54 = 6 × 9

6 12 18 24 30 36 42 48 54

9 18 27 36 45 54

9

6

54

6 × 8 = 48

8 × 6 = 48

8 16 24 32 40 48

6 12 18 24 30 36 42 48

8

6

48

7×9 9×7	$\begin{array}{r} 8 \\ \times\ 8 \\ \hline \end{array}$	9×8 8×9	$\begin{array}{r} 9 \\ \times\ 9 \\ \hline \end{array}$

81 = 9 × 9

9
18
27
36
45

54
63
72
81

9

9 81

9	8
× 8	× 9
72	72

8	9
16	18
24	27
32	36
40	45
48	54
56	63
64	72
72	

9

8 72

64 = 8 × 8

8
16
24
32
40

48
56
64

8

8 64

7	9
× 9	× 7
63	63

9	7
18	14
27	21
36	28
45	35
54	42
63	49
	56
	63

9

7 63

$2\overline{)4}$ $4 \div 2$	$2\overline{)6}$ $6 \div 2$	$2\overline{)8}$ $8 \div 2$	$2\overline{)10}$ $10 \div 2$
$2\overline{)12}$ $12 \div 2$	$2\overline{)14}$ $14 \div 2$	$2\overline{)16}$ $16 \div 2$	$2\overline{)18}$ $18 \div 2$

$2\overline{)10}$ = 5 $5\overline{)10}$ = 2

2
4
6
8
10

5
10

5
2 10

$2\overline{)8}$ = 4 $4\overline{)8}$ = 2

2
4
6
8

4
8

4
2 8

$2\overline{)6}$ = 3 $3\overline{)6}$ = 2

2
4
6

3
6

3
2 6

$2\overline{)4}$ = 2

2
4

2
2 4

$2\overline{)18}$ = 9 $9\overline{)18}$ = 2

2
4
6
8
10
12
14
16
18

9
18

9
2 18

$2\overline{)16}$ = 8 $8\overline{)16}$ = 2

2
4
6
8
10
12
14
16

8
16

8
2 16

$2\overline{)14}$ = 7 $7\overline{)14}$ = 2

2
4
6
8
10
12
14

7
14

7
2 14

$2\overline{)12}$ = 6 $6\overline{)12}$ = 2

2
4
6
8
10
12

6
12

6
2 12

$3\overline{)6}$

$6 \div 3$

$4\overline{)8}$

$8 \div 4$

$5\overline{)10}$

$10 \div 5$

$6\overline{)12}$

$12 \div 6$

$7\overline{)14}$

$14 \div 7$

$8\overline{)16}$

$16 \div 8$

$9\overline{)18}$

$18 \div 9$

$3\overline{)9}$

$9 \div 3$

$$6\overline{)12}\quad 2$$ $$2\overline{)12}\quad 6$$

6
12

2
4
6
8
10
12

2
6 12

$$5\overline{)10}\quad 2$$ $$2\overline{)10}\quad 5$$

5
10

2
4
6
8
10

2
5 10

$$4\overline{)8}\quad 2$$ $$2\overline{)8}\quad 4$$

4
8

2
4
6
8

2
4 8

$$3\overline{)6}\quad 2$$ $$2\overline{)6}\quad 3$$

3
6

2
4
6

2
3 6

$$3\overline{)9}\quad 3$$

3
6
9

3
3 9

$$9\overline{)18}\quad 2$$ $$2\overline{)18}\quad 9$$

9
18

2
4
6
8
10
12
14
16
18

2
9 18

$$8\overline{)16}\quad 2$$ $$2\overline{)16}\quad 8$$

8
16

2
4
6
8
10
12
14
16

2
8 16

$$7\overline{)14}\quad 2$$ $$2\overline{)14}\quad 7$$

7
14

2
4
6
8
10
12
14

2
7 14

$3\overline{)12}$

$12 \div 3$

$3\overline{)15}$

$15 \div 3$

$3\overline{)18}$

$18 \div 3$

$3\overline{)21}$

$21 \div 3$

$3\overline{)24}$

$24 \div 3$

$3\overline{)27}$

$27 \div 3$

$4\overline{)12}$

$12 \div 4$

$5\overline{)15}$

$15 \div 5$

$\begin{array}{r}7\\3\overline{)21}\end{array}$ $\begin{array}{r}3\\7\overline{)21}\end{array}$

3
6
9
12
15
18
21

7
14
21

7
3 | 21

$\begin{array}{r}6\\3\overline{)18}\end{array}$ $\begin{array}{r}3\\6\overline{)18}\end{array}$

3
6
9
12
15
18

6
12
18

6
3 | 18

$\begin{array}{r}5\\3\overline{)15}\end{array}$ $\begin{array}{r}3\\5\overline{)15}\end{array}$

3
6
9
12
15

5
10
15

5
3 | 15

$\begin{array}{r}4\\3\overline{)12}\end{array}$ $\begin{array}{r}3\\4\overline{)12}\end{array}$

3
6
9
12

4
8
12

4
3 | 12

$\begin{array}{r}3\\5\overline{)15}\end{array}$ $\begin{array}{r}5\\3\overline{)15}\end{array}$

5
10
15

3
6
9
12
15

3
5 | 15

$\begin{array}{r}3\\4\overline{)12}\end{array}$ $\begin{array}{r}4\\3\overline{)12}\end{array}$

4
8
12

3
6
9
12

3
4 | 12

$\begin{array}{r}9\\3\overline{)27}\end{array}$ $\begin{array}{r}3\\9\overline{)27}\end{array}$

3
6
9
12
15
18
21
24
27

9
18
27

9
3 | 27

$\begin{array}{r}8\\3\overline{)24}\end{array}$ $\begin{array}{r}3\\8\overline{)24}\end{array}$

3
6
9
12
15
18
21
24

8
16
24

8
3 | 24

$6\overline{)18}$ $18 \div 6$	$7\overline{)21}$ $21 \div 7$	$8\overline{)24}$ $24 \div 8$	$9\overline{)27}$ $27 \div 9$
$4\overline{)16}$ $16 \div 4$	$4\overline{)20}$ $20 \div 4$	$4\overline{)24}$ $24 \div 4$	$4\overline{)28}$ $28 \div 4$

$9\overline{)27} = 3$ $3\overline{)27} = 9$

9
18
27

3
6
9
12
15

18
21
24
27

3

9 27

$8\overline{)24} = 3$ $3\overline{)24} = 8$

8
16
24

3
6
9
12
15

18
21
24

3

8 24

$7\overline{)21} = 3$ $3\overline{)21} = 7$

7
14
21

3
6
9
12
15

18
21

3

7 21

$6\overline{)18} = 3$ $3\overline{)18} = 6$

6
12
18

3
6
9
12
15

18

3

6 18

$4\overline{)28} = 7$ $7\overline{)28} = 4$

4
8
12
16
20

24
28

7
14
21
28

7

4 28

$4\overline{)24} = 6$ $6\overline{)24} = 4$

4
8
12
16
20

24

6
12
18
24

6

4 24

$4\overline{)20} = 5$ $5\overline{)20} = 4$

4
8
12
16
20

5
10
15
20

5

4 20

$4\overline{)16} = 4$

4
8
12
16

4

4 16

$4\overline{)32}$ $32 \div 4$	$4\overline{)36}$ $36 \div 4$	$5\overline{)20}$ $20 \div 5$	$6\overline{)24}$ $24 \div 6$
$7\overline{)28}$ $28 \div 7$	$8\overline{)32}$ $32 \div 8$	$9\overline{)36}$ $36 \div 9$	$5\overline{)25}$ $25 \div 5$

$6\overline{)24}$ = 4 | $4\overline{)24}$ = 6

6, 12, 18, 24 | 4, 8, 12, 16, 20, 24

4 × 6 array: 24

$5\overline{)20}$ = 4 | $4\overline{)20}$ = 5

5, 10, 15, 20 | 4, 8, 12, 16, 20

4 × 5 array: 20

$4\overline{)36}$ = 9 | $9\overline{)36}$ = 4

4, 8, 12, 16, 20, 24, 28, 32, 36 | 9, 18, 27, 36

9 × 4 array: 36

$4\overline{)32}$ = 8 | $8\overline{)32}$ = 4

4, 8, 12, 16, 20, 24, 28, 32 | 8, 16, 24, 32

8 × 4 array: 32

$5\overline{)25}$ = 5

5, 10, 15, 20, 25

5 × 5 array: 25

$9\overline{)36}$ = 4 | $4\overline{)36}$ = 9

9, 18, 27, 36 | 4, 8, 12, 16, 20, 24, 28, 32, 36

4 × 9 array: 36

$8\overline{)32}$ = 4 | $4\overline{)32}$ = 8

8, 16, 24, 32 | 4, 8, 12, 16, 20, 24, 28, 32

4 × 8 array: 32

$7\overline{)28}$ = 4 | $4\overline{)28}$ = 7

7, 14, 21, 28 | 4, 8, 12, 16, 20, 24, 28

4 × 7 array: 28

$5\overline{)30}$ $30 \div 5$	$5\overline{)35}$ $35 \div 5$	$5\overline{)40}$ $40 \div 5$	$5\overline{)45}$ $45 \div 5$
$6\overline{)30}$ $30 \div 6$	$7\overline{)35}$ $35 \div 7$	$8\overline{)40}$ $40 \div 8$	$9\overline{)45}$ $45 \div 9$

$\begin{array}{r}9\\5\overline{)45}\end{array}$ $\begin{array}{r}5\\9\overline{)45}\end{array}$

5	9
10	18
15	27
20	36
25	45
30	
35	
40	
45	

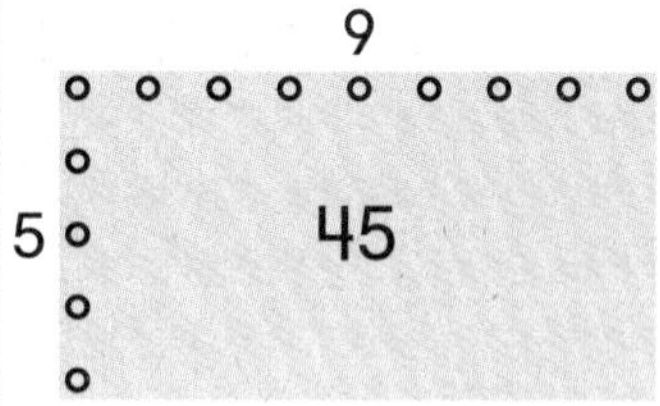

$\begin{array}{r}8\\5\overline{)40}\end{array}$ $\begin{array}{r}5\\8\overline{)40}\end{array}$

5	8
10	16
15	24
20	32
25	40
30	
35	
40	

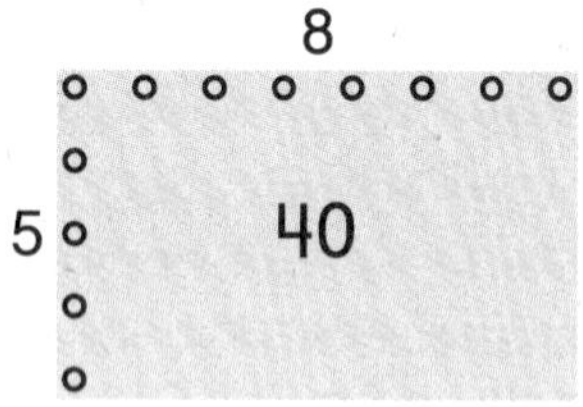

$\begin{array}{r}7\\5\overline{)35}\end{array}$ $\begin{array}{r}5\\7\overline{)35}\end{array}$

5	7
10	14
15	21
20	28
25	35
30	
35	

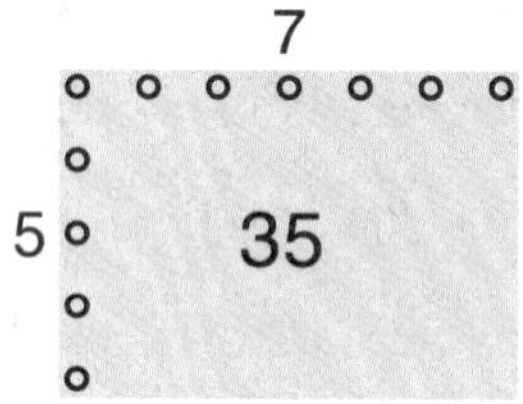

$\begin{array}{r}6\\5\overline{)30}\end{array}$ $\begin{array}{r}5\\6\overline{)30}\end{array}$

5	6
10	12
15	18
20	24
25	30
30	

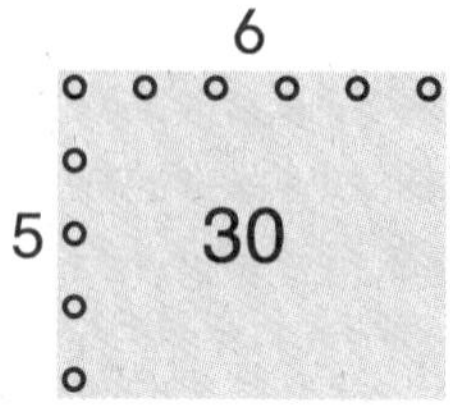

$\begin{array}{r}5\\9\overline{)45}\end{array}$ $\begin{array}{r}9\\5\overline{)45}\end{array}$

9	5
18	10
27	15
36	20
45	25
	30
	35
	40
	45

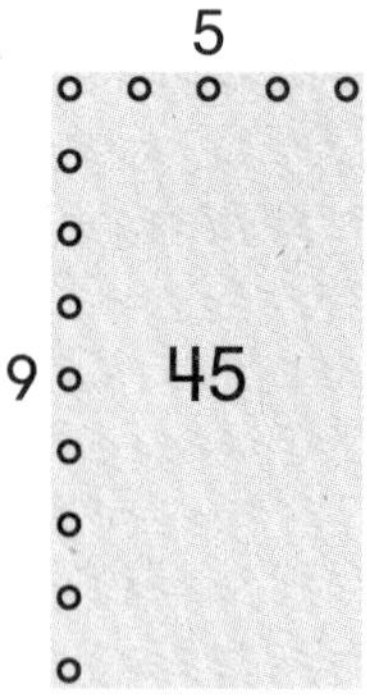

$\begin{array}{r}5\\8\overline{)40}\end{array}$ $\begin{array}{r}8\\5\overline{)40}\end{array}$

8	5
16	10
24	15
32	20
40	25
	30
	35
	40

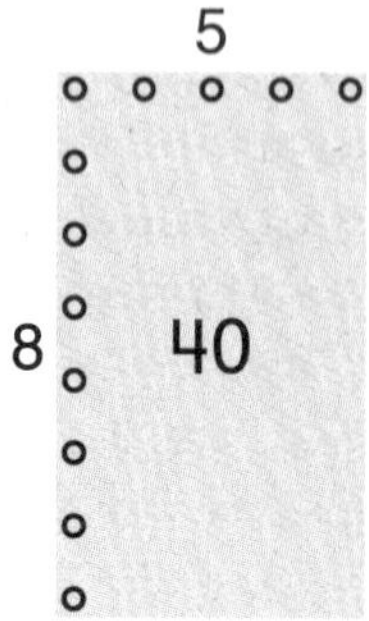

$\begin{array}{r}5\\7\overline{)35}\end{array}$ $\begin{array}{r}7\\5\overline{)35}\end{array}$

7	5
14	10
21	15
28	20
35	25
	30
	35

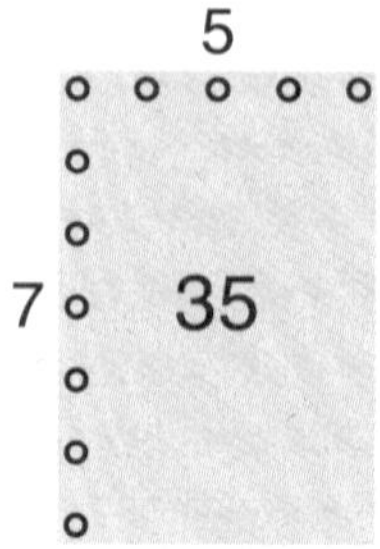

$\begin{array}{r}5\\6\overline{)30}\end{array}$ $\begin{array}{r}6\\5\overline{)30}\end{array}$

6	5
12	10
18	15
24	20
30	25
	30

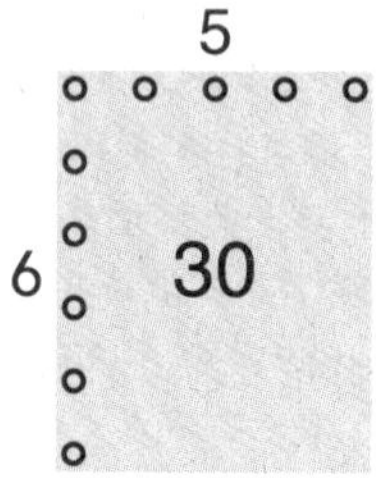

$6\overline{)36}$

$36 \div 6$

$6\overline{)42}$

$42 \div 6$

$6\overline{)48}$

$48 \div 6$

$6\overline{)54}$

$54 \div 6$

$7\overline{)42}$

$42 \div 7$

$8\overline{)48}$

$48 \div 8$

$9\overline{)54}$

$54 \div 9$

$7\overline{)49}$

$49 \div 7$

$6\overline{)54}$ = 9 $9\overline{)54}$ = 6

6
12
18
24
30

36
42
48
54

9
18
27
36
45

54

9

6 54

$6\overline{)48}$ = 8 $8\overline{)48}$ = 6

6
12
18
24
30

36
42
48

8
16
24
32
40

48

8

6 48

$6\overline{)42}$ = 7 $7\overline{)42}$ = 6

6
12
18
24
30

36
42

7
14
21
28
35

42

7

6 42

$6\overline{)36}$ = 6

6
12
18
24
30

36

6

6 36

$7\overline{)49}$ = 7

7
14
21
28
35

42
49

7

7 49

$9\overline{)54}$ = 6 $6\overline{)54}$ = 9

9
18
27
36
45

54

6
12
18
24
30

36
42
48
54

6

9 54

$8\overline{)48}$ = 6 $6\overline{)48}$ = 8

8
16
24
32
40

48

6
12
18
24
30

36
42
48

6

8 48

$7\overline{)42}$ = 6 $6\overline{)42}$ = 7

7
14
21
28
35

42

6
12
18
24
30

36
42

6

7 42

$7\overline{)56}$

$56 \div 7$

$7\overline{)63}$

$63 \div 7$

$8\overline{)56}$

$56 \div 8$

$9\overline{)63}$

$63 \div 9$

$8\overline{)64}$

$64 \div 8$

$8\overline{)72}$

$72 \div 8$

$9\overline{)72}$

$72 \div 9$

$9\overline{)81}$

$81 \div 9$

$9\overline{)63}$ = 7 $7\overline{)63}$ = 9

9
18
27
36
45

54
63

7
14
21
28
35

42
49
56
63

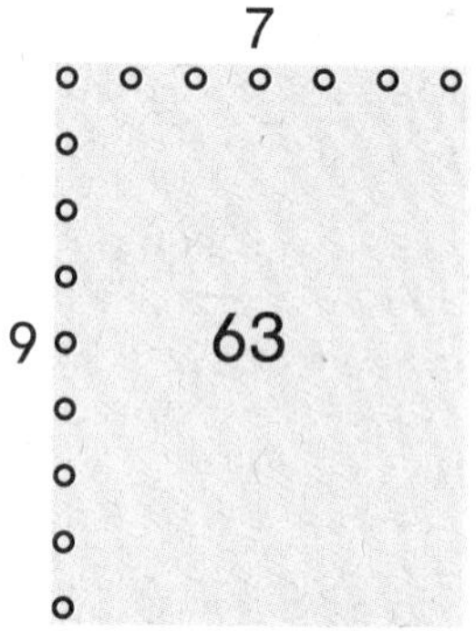

7
9 | 63

$8\overline{)56}$ = 7 $7\overline{)56}$ = 8

8
16
24
32
40

48
56

7
14
21
28
35

42
49
56

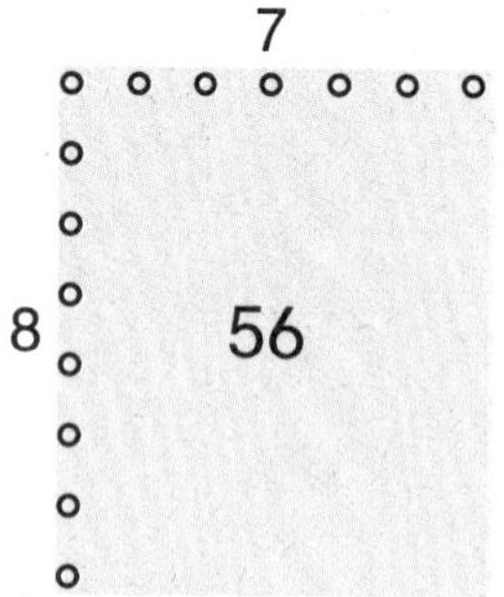

7
8 | 56

$7\overline{)63}$ = 9 $9\overline{)63}$ = 7

7
14
21
28
35

42
49
56
63

9
18
27
36
45

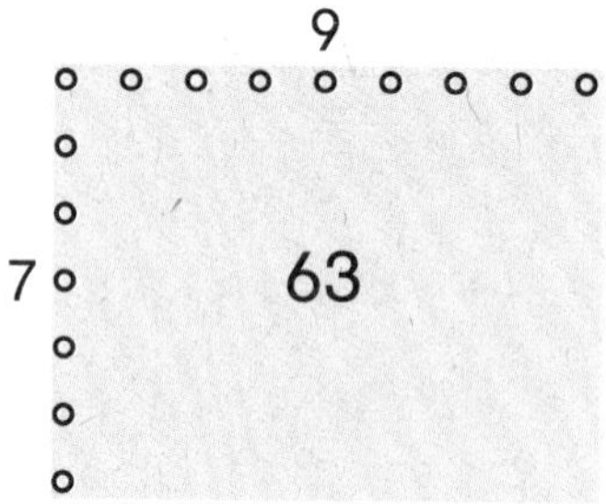

54
63

9
7 | 63

$7\overline{)56}$ = 8 $8\overline{)56}$ = 7

7
14
21
28
35

42
49
56

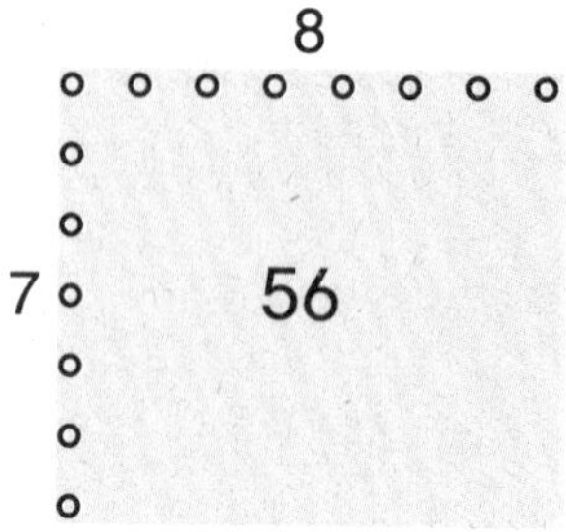

8
16
24
32
40

48
56

8
7 | 56

$9\overline{)81}$ = 9

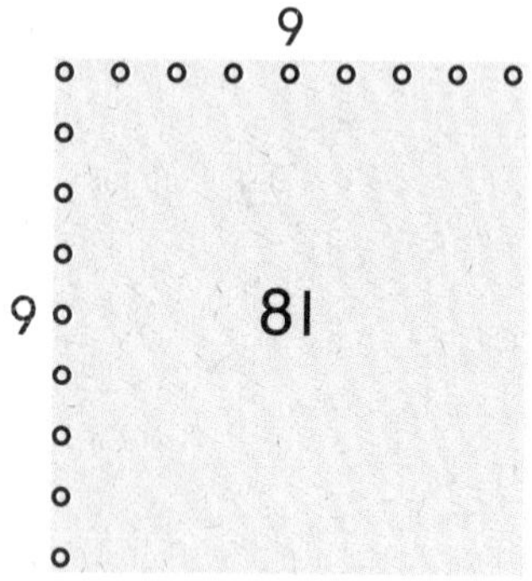

9
18
27
36
45

54
63
72
81

9
9 | 81

$9\overline{)72}$ = 8 $8\overline{)72}$ = 9

9
18
27
36
45

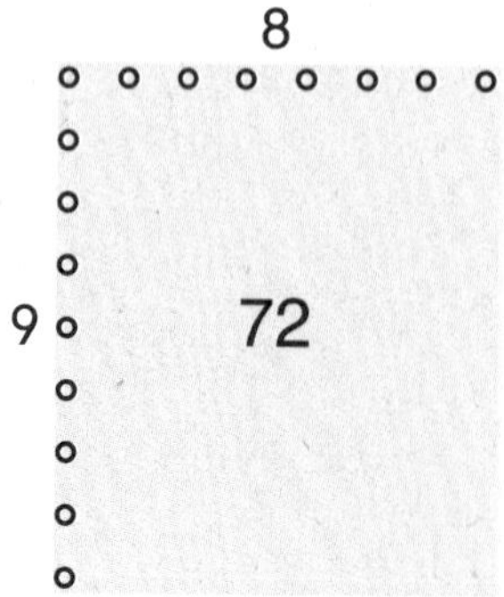

54
63
72

8
16
24
32
40

48
56
64
72

8
9 | 72

$8\overline{)72}$ = 9 $9\overline{)72}$ = 8

8
16
24
32
40

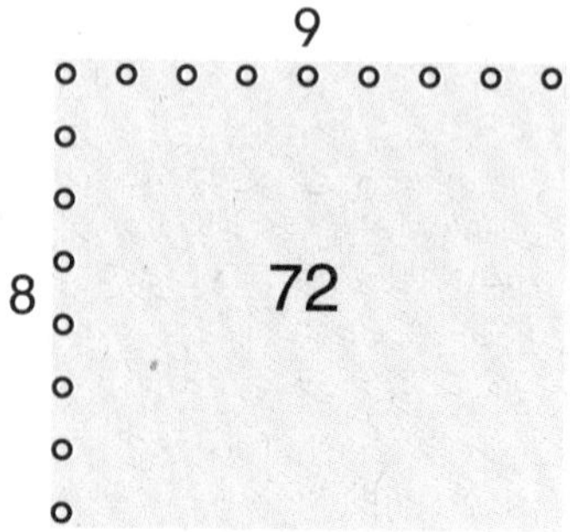

48
56
64
72

9
18
27
36
45

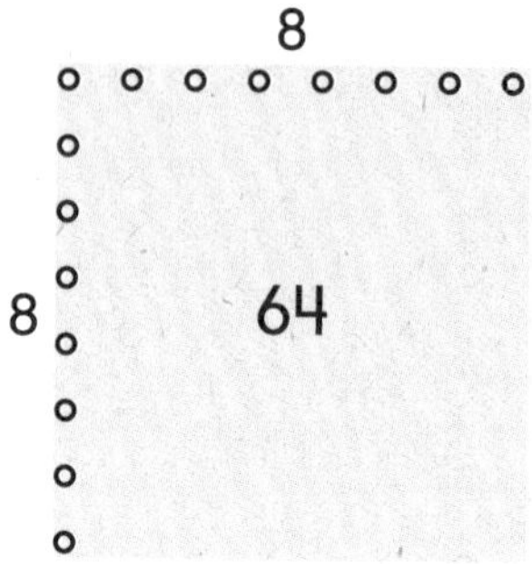

54
63
72

9
8 | 72

$8\overline{)64}$ = 8

8
16
24
32
40

48
56
64

8
8 | 64

Name ______________________

PATH to FLUENCY

Check Sheet 4: 3s and 4s

3s Multiplications	3s Divisions	4s Multiplications	4s Divisions
8 × 3 = 24	9 / 3 = 3	1 × 4 = 4	40 / 4 = 10
3 • 2 = 6	21 ÷ 3 = 7	4 • 5 = 20	12 ÷ 4 = 3
3 * 5 = 15	27 / 3 = 9	8 * 4 = 32	24 / 4 = 6
10 × 3 = 30	3 ÷ 3 = 1	3 × 4 = 12	8 ÷ 4 = 2
3 • 3 = 9	18 / 3 = 6	4 • 6 = 24	4 / 4 = 1
3 * 6 = 18	12 ÷ 3 = 4	4 * 9 = 36	28 ÷ 4 = 7
7 × 3 = 21	30 / 3 = 10	10 × 4 = 40	32 / 4 = 8
3 • 9 = 27	6 ÷ 3 = 2	4 • 7 = 28	16 ÷ 4 = 4
4 * 3 = 12	24 / 3 = 8	4 * 4 = 16	36 / 4 = 9
3 × 1 = 3	15 / 3 = 5	2 × 4 = 8	20 / 4 = 5
3 • 4 = 12	21 ÷ 3 = 7	4 • 3 = 12	4 ÷ 4 = 1
3 * 3 = 9	3 / 3 = 1	4 * 2 = 8	32 / 4 = 8
3 × 10 = 30	9 ÷ 3 = 3	9 × 4 = 36	8 ÷ 4 = 2
2 • 3 = 6	27 / 3 = 9	1 • 4 = 4	16 / 4 = 4
3 * 7 = 21	30 ÷ 3 = 10	4 * 6 = 24	36 ÷ 4 = 9
6 × 3 = 18	18 / 3 = 6	5 × 4 = 20	12 / 4 = 3
5 • 3 = 15	6 ÷ 3 = 2	4 • 4 = 16	40 ÷ 4 = 10
3 * 8 = 24	15 ÷ 3 = 5	7 * 4 = 28	20 ÷ 4 = 5
9 × 3 = 27	12 / 3 = 4	8 × 4 = 32	24 / 4 = 6
2 • 3 = 6	24 ÷ 3 = 8	10 • 4 = 40	28 ÷ 4 = 7

 Name ____________________

Make Sense of Problems

Write an equation and solve the problem.

Show your work.

1. The garden shop received a shipment of 12 rose bushes. They arranged the rose bushes in 3 rows with the same number of bushes in each row. How many rose bushes were in each row?

   ____

2. Eric saw 4 stop signs on the way to school. Each stop sign had 8 sides. How many sides were on all 4 stop signs?

   ____

3. Ed needs 14 batteries. If he buys the batteries in packages of 2, how many packages of batteries will he need to buy?

   ____

4. A flag has 5 rows of stars with the same number of stars in each row. There are 35 stars on the flag. How many stars are in each row?

   ____

5. Melia learned in science class that insects have 6 legs. What is the total number of legs on 9 insects?

   ____

6. Stan has 4 model car kits. Each kit comes with 5 tires. How many tires does Stan have altogether?

   ____

Make Sense of Problems (continued)

Write an equation and solve the problem.

Show your work.

7 Maria bought a shoe rack. The shoe rack has 3 rows with places for 6 shoes on each row. How many shoes can be placed on the shoe rack?

____

8 The park has 4 swing sets with the same number of swings on each set. There is a total of 16 swings at the park. How many swings are on each swing set?

____

9 Amanda has 27 seashells in her collection. She displayed the seashells in 3 rows with the same number of seashells in each row. How many seashells are in each row?

____

10 The art room has 4 round tables. There are 6 chairs around each table. Altogether, how many chairs are around the tables?

____

11 Shanna is making bead necklaces for the craft fair. She can make 3 necklaces a day. She plans to make 21 necklaces. How many days will it take her to make the necklaces?

____

Check Understanding

What four equations can you write for this fast array drawing?

7
○ ○ ○ ○ ○ ○ ○
3 ○ 21
○

____

Use the Strategy Cards

Name ______________________________

PATH to FLUENCY Play *Solve the Stack*

Read the rules for playing *Solve the Stack*. Then play the game with your group.

Rules for *Solve the Stack*

Number of players: 2–4

What you will need: 1 set of Multiplication and Division Strategy Cards

1. Shuffle the cards. Place them exercise side up in the center of the table.
2. Players take turns. On each turn, a player finds the answer to the multiplication or division on the top card and then turns the card over to check the answer.
3. If a player's answer is correct, he or she takes the card. If it is incorrect, the card is placed at the bottom of the stack.
4. Play ends when there are no more cards in the stack. The player with the most cards wins.

PATH to FLUENCY Play *High Card Wins*

Read the rules for playing *High Card Wins*. Then play the game with your partner.

Rules for *High Card Wins*

Number of players: 2

What you will need: 1 set of Multiplication and Division Strategy Cards for 2s, 3s, 4s, 5s, 9s

1. Shuffle the cards. Deal all the cards evenly between the two players.
2. Players put their stacks in front of them, exercise side up.
3. Each player takes the top card from his or her stack and puts it exercise side up in the center of the table.
4. Each player says the multiplication or division answer and then turns the card over to check. Then players do one of the following:
    - If one player says the wrong answer, the other player takes both cards and puts them at the bottom of his or her pile.
    - If both players say the wrong answer, both players take back their cards and put them at the bottom of their piles.
    - If both players say the correct answer, the player with the higher product or quotient takes both cards and puts them at the bottom of his or her pile. If the products or quotients are the same, the players set the cards aside and play another round. The winner of the next round takes all the cards.
5. Play continues until one player has all the cards.

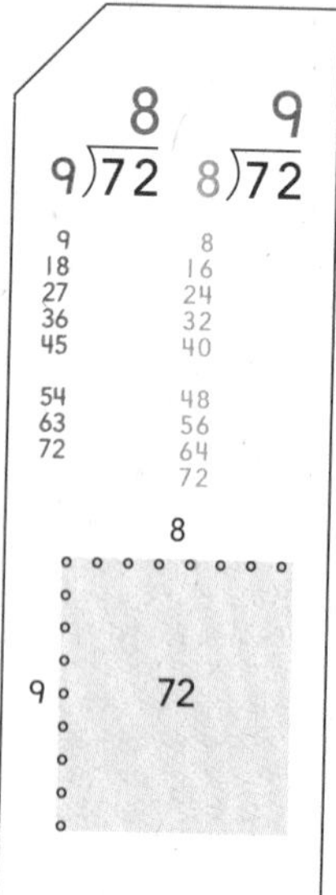

 Name ______________

PATH to FLUENCY Review Strategies

Answer the questions.

1. Emily knows that $4 \times 10 = 40$. How can she use subtraction and multiples of 9 to find 4×9?

____

____

2. Joey knows the multiplications 5×4 and 4×4. How can he use their products to find 9×4?

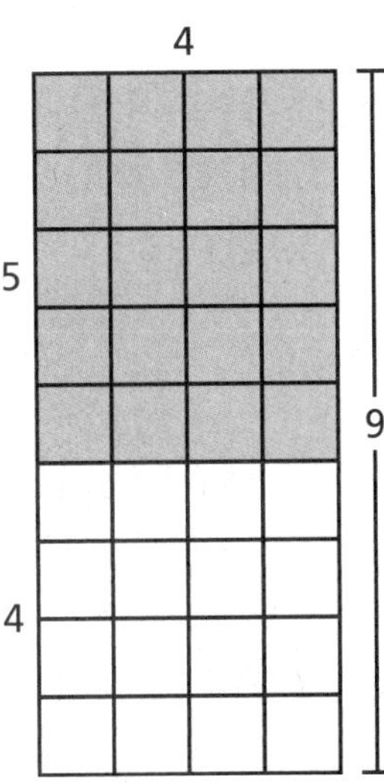

____

3. Hannah knows that each division has a related multiplication. What related multiplication can she use to find $18 \div 3$?

____

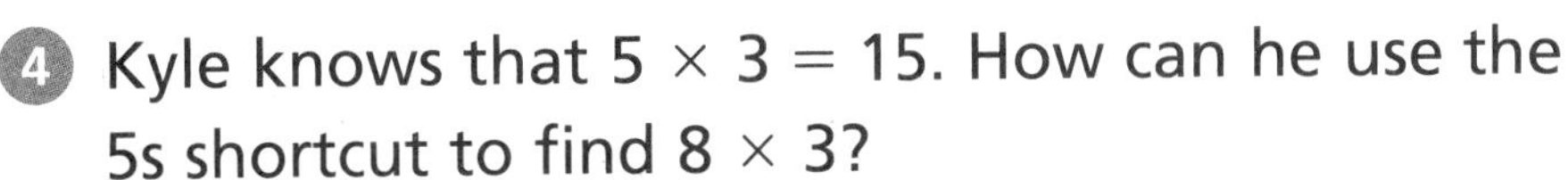

4. Kyle knows that $5 \times 3 = 15$. How can he use the 5s shortcut to find 8×3?

____

____

5. Letitia knows that $5 \times 4 = 20$. How can she use the 5s shortcut to find 9×4?

____

____

6. Jorge knows that $6 \times 9 = 54$. How can he use the Commutative Property or arrays to find 9×6?

____

____

____

Make Sense of Problems

Write an equation and solve the problem.

Show your work.

7. Jordan has 32 peaches. He wants to divide them equally among 4 baskets. How many peaches will he put in each basket?

______

8. A guitar has 6 strings. If Taylor replaces all the strings on 3 guitars, how many strings does he need?

______

9. Kassler puts 5 strawberries in each bowl. Kassler has 40 strawberries. How many bowls will he fill?

______

10. Ruel has a board 36 inches long. He wants to saw it into equal pieces 9 inches long. How many pieces will he get?

______

Write a Word Problem

11. Write a word problem that can be solved using the equation $7 \times 10 = 70$.

______

______

______

Check Understanding

What strategy did you use to solve Problem 10?

______

Name ______________________________

Explore Patterns with 1s

What patterns do you see below?

1

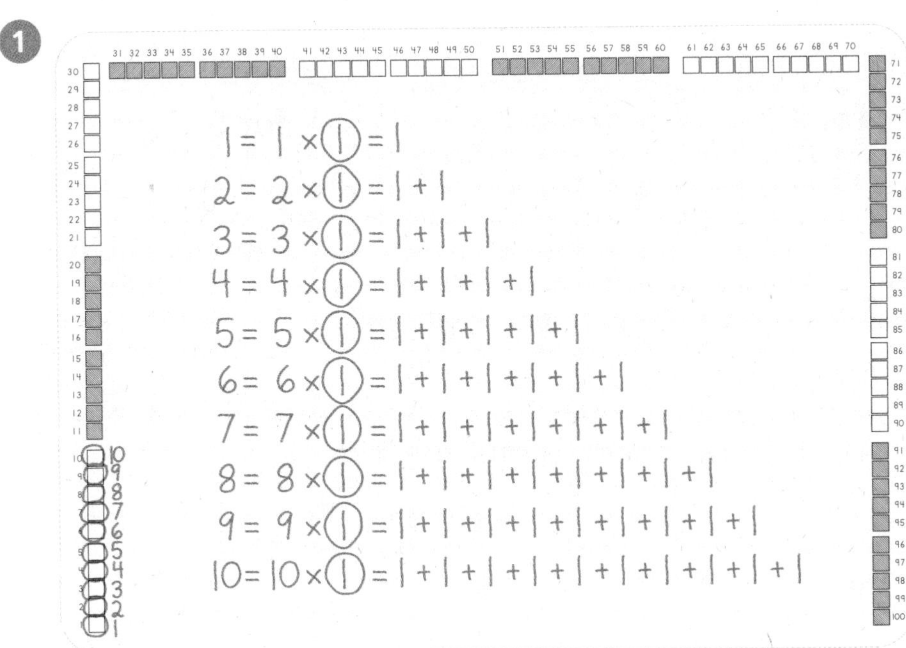

Explore Patterns with 0s

What patterns do you see below?

2

$1 \times 0 = 0$

$2 \times 0 = 0 + 0$

$3 \times 0 = 0 + 0 + 0$

$4 \times 0 = 0 + 0 + 0 + 0$

$5 \times 0 = 0 + 0 + 0 + 0 + 0$

$6 \times 0 = 0 + 0 + 0 + 0 + 0 + 0$

$7 \times 0 = 0 + 0 + 0 + 0 + 0 + 0 + 0$

$8 \times 0 = 0 + 0 + 0 + 0 + 0 + 0 + 0 + 0$

$9 \times 0 = 0 + 0 + 0 + 0 + 0 + 0 + 0 + 0 + 0$

$10 \times 0 = 0 + 0 + 0 + 0 + 0 + 0 + 0 + 0 + 0 + 0$

PATH to FLUENCY Multiplication Properties and Division Rules

Properties and Rules

Property for 1	Division Rule for 1	Zero Property	Division Rule for 0
$1 \times 6 = 6$	$8 \div 1 = 8$	$6 \times 0 = 0$	$0 \div 6 = 0$
$6 \times 1 = 6$	$8 \div 8 = 1$	$0 \times 6 = 0$	$6 \div 0$ is impossible.

Associative Property of Multiplication

When you group factors in different ways, the product stays the same. The parentheses tell you which numbers to multiply first.

$(3 \times 2) \times 5 = \square$

$6 \times 5 = 30$

$3 \times (2 \times 5) = \square$

$3 \times 10 = 30$

Find each product.

3 $2 \times (6 \times 1) = \square$

4 $(4 \times 2) \times 2 = \square$

5 $7 \times (1 \times 5) = \square$

6 $(9 \times 8) \times 0 = \square$

7 $3 \times (2 \times 3) = \square$

8 $6 \times (0 \times 7) = \square$

Solve each problem.

Show your work.

9 Shawn gave 1 nickel to each of his sisters. If he gave away 3 nickels, how many sisters does Shawn have? ____________

10 Kara has 3 empty boxes. She put 0 toys in each box. How many toys are in the boxes? ____________

11 There are 3 shelves in a bookshelf. Each shelf has 2 piles of books on it. If there are 3 books in each pile, how many books are in the bookshelf?

____

Name ___

PATH to FLUENCY

Identify Addition and Multiplication Properties

Addition Properties

A. Commutative Property of Addition The order in which numbers are added does not change their sum.

$$3 + 5 = 5 + 3$$

B. Associative Property of Addition The way in which numbers are grouped does not change their sum.

$$(3 + 2) + 5 = 3 + (2 + 5)$$

C. Identity Property of Addition If 0 is added to a number, the sum equals that number.

$$3 + 0 = 3$$

Multiplication Properties

D. Commutative Property of Multiplication The order in which numbers are multiplied does not change their product.

$$3 \times 5 = 5 \times 3$$

E. Associative Property of Multiplication The way in which numbers are grouped does not change their product.

$$(3 \times 2) \times 5 = 3 \times (2 \times 5)$$

F. Identity Property of Multiplication The product of 1 and any number is that number.

$$3 \times 1 = 3$$

G. Zero Property of Multiplication If 0 is multiplied by a number, the product is 0.

$$3 \times 0 = 0$$

Write the letter of the property that is shown.

12. $1 \times 9 = 9$ ___

13. $5 + (6 + 7) = (5 + 6) + 7$ ___

14. $5 \times 0 = 0$ ___

15. $8 + 0 = 8$ ___

16. $3 \times 9 = 9 \times 3$ ___

17. $(2 \times 1) \times 3 = 2 \times (1 \times 3)$ ___

PATH to FLUENCY Use Properties to Solve Equations

Use properties and rules to find the unknown numbers.

18 $5 \times 8 = \square \times 5$

19 $4 + 3 = \square + 4$

20 $0 \div 8 = \square$

21 $4 \div 4 = \square$

22 $(3 \times 2) \times 4 = 3 \times (\square \times 4)$

23 $6 \times 2 = 2 \times \square$

24 $5 \times 3 = \square \times 5$

25 $(6 + 2) + 2 = 6 + (\square + 2)$

26 $11 + 0 = \square$

27 $65 \times 1 = \square$

28 $5 \times (2 \times 6) = (5 \times 2) \times \square$

29 $17 \times 0 = \square$

Use Equations to Demonstrate Properties

Write your own equation that shows the property.

30 Commutative Property of Multiplication

31 Associative Property of Addition

32 Identity Property of Addition

33 Identity Property of Multiplication

34 Associative Property of Multiplication

35 Zero Property of Multiplication

36 Commutative Property of Addition

Check Understanding

Explain what you know about multiplying or dividing a number by 1 and multiplying or dividing a number by 0.

Name ______________________

PATH to FLUENCY

Check Sheet 5: 1s and 0s

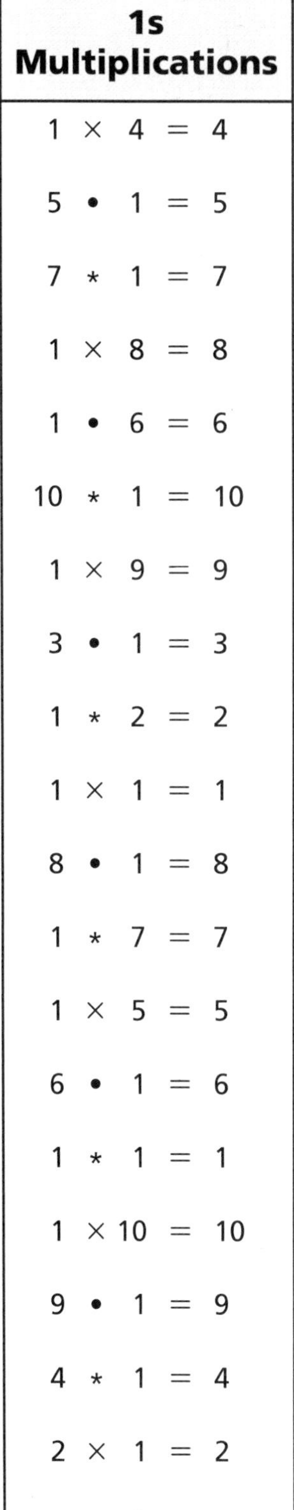

1s Multiplications	1s Divisions	0s Multiplications
1 × 4 = 4	10 / 1 = 10	4 × 0 = 0
5 • 1 = 5	5 ÷ 1 = 5	2 • 0 = 0
7 * 1 = 7	7 / 1 = 7	0 * 8 = 0
1 × 8 = 8	9 ÷ 1 = 9	0 × 5 = 0
1 • 6 = 6	3 / 1 = 3	6 • 0 = 0
10 * 1 = 10	10 ÷ 1 = 10	0 * 7 = 0
1 × 9 = 9	2 / 1 = 2	0 × 2 = 0
3 • 1 = 3	8 ÷ 1 = 8	0 • 9 = 0
1 * 2 = 2	6 / 1 = 6	10 * 0 = 0
1 × 1 = 1	9 / 1 = 9	1 × 0 = 0
8 • 1 = 8	1 ÷ 1 = 1	0 • 6 = 0
1 * 7 = 7	5 / 1 = 5	9 * 0 = 0
1 × 5 = 5	3 ÷ 1 = 3	0 × 4 = 0
6 • 1 = 6	4 / 1 = 4	3 • 0 = 0
1 * 1 = 1	2 ÷ 1 = 2	0 * 3 = 0
1 × 10 = 10	8 / 1 = 8	8 × 0 = 0
9 • 1 = 9	4 ÷ 1 = 4	0 • 10 = 0
4 * 1 = 4	7 ÷ 1 = 7	0 * 1 = 0
2 × 1 = 2	1 / 1 = 1	5 × 0 = 0
1 • 3 = 3	6 ÷ 1 = 6	7 • 0 = 0

PATH to FLUENCY Check Sheet 6: Mixed 3s, 4s, 0s, and 1s

3s, 4s, 0s, 1s Multiplications
5 × 3 = 15
6 • 4 = 24
9 * 0 = 0
7 × 1 = 7
3 • 3 = 9
4 * 7 = 28
0 × 10 = 0
1 • 6 = 6
3 * 4 = 12
5 × 4 = 20
0 • 5 = 0
9 * 1 = 9
2 × 3 = 6
3 • 4 = 12
0 * 9 = 0
1 × 5 = 5
2 • 3 = 6
4 * 4 = 16
9 × 0 = 0
1 • 1 = 1

3s, 4s, 0s, 1s Multiplications
0 × 5 = 0
10 • 1 = 10
6 * 3 = 18
2 × 4 = 8
5 • 0 = 0
1 * 2 = 2
10 × 3 = 30
5 • 4 = 20
0 * 8 = 0
9 × 1 = 9
10 • 3 = 30
9 * 4 = 36
1 × 0 = 0
1 • 6 = 6
3 * 6 = 18
7 × 4 = 28
6 • 0 = 0
8 * 1 = 8
3 × 9 = 27
1 • 4 = 4

3s, 4s, 1s Divisions
18 / 3 = 6
20 ÷ 4 = 5
1 / 1 = 1
21 ÷ 3 = 7
12 / 4 = 3
5 ÷ 1 = 5
15 / 3 = 5
24 ÷ 4 = 6
7 / 1 = 7
12 / 3 = 4
36 ÷ 4 = 9
6 / 1 = 6
12 ÷ 3 = 4
16 / 4 = 4
7 ÷ 1 = 7
9 / 3 = 3
8 ÷ 4 = 2
2 ÷ 1 = 2
6 / 3 = 2
32 ÷ 4 = 8

3s, 4s, 1s Divisions
4 / 1 = 4
21 ÷ 3 = 7
16 / 4 = 4
9 ÷ 1 = 9
15 / 3 = 5
8 ÷ 4 = 2
5 / 1 = 5
30 ÷ 3 = 10
12 / 4 = 3
8 / 1 = 8
27 ÷ 3 = 9
40 / 4 = 10
4 ÷ 1 = 4
9 / 3 = 3
16 ÷ 4 = 4
10 / 1 = 10
9 ÷ 3 = 3
20 ÷ 4 = 5
6 / 1 = 6
24 ÷ 3 = 8

Name ____________________

Write and Solve Equations

Write an equation and solve the problem.

Show your work.

1. The library ordered 1 computer for each of the work stations. If the library ordered 8 computers, how many work stations are in the library?

   ____

   ____

2. Ari arranged his baseball cap collection into 9 rows with 2 baseball caps in each row. How many baseball caps are in his collection?

   ____

   ____

3. Jess solved 28 multiplication problems. If the problems were arranged in columns with 7 problems in each column, how many columns of problems did Jess solve?

   ____

   ____

4. One section on a plane has 9 rows of seats. Five passengers can sit in each row. How many passengers can sit in this section of the plane?

   ____

   ____

5. Emily rides her bike 3 miles every day. How many miles does she ride her bike in a week?

   ____

   ____

Solve and Discuss

Write an equation and solve the problem.

Show your work.

6 Paige placed 35 books on 5 shelves. She placed the same number of books on each shelf. How many books did she place on each shelf?

7 A box of bagels has 24 bagels. There are 4 bagels in each row. How many rows of bagels are in the box?

8 Keshawn bought 18 animal stickers for his sisters. He gave 6 stickers to each sister and had none left. How many sisters does Keshawn have?

Write a Word Problem

9 Write a word problem that can be solved using $4 \div 1$, where 1 is the group size.

Check Understanding

Write two multiplication equations and two division equations using the numbers 8, 4, and 2 in each.

Name ______________________________

PATH to FLUENCY Play *Multiplication Three-in-a-Row*

Read the rules for playing *Multiplication Three-in-a-Row*. Then play the game with a partner.

Rules for *Multiplication Three-in-a-Row*

Number of players: 2

What You Will Need: A set of Multiplication Strategy Cards, *Three-in-a-Row* Game Grids for each player (see page 83)

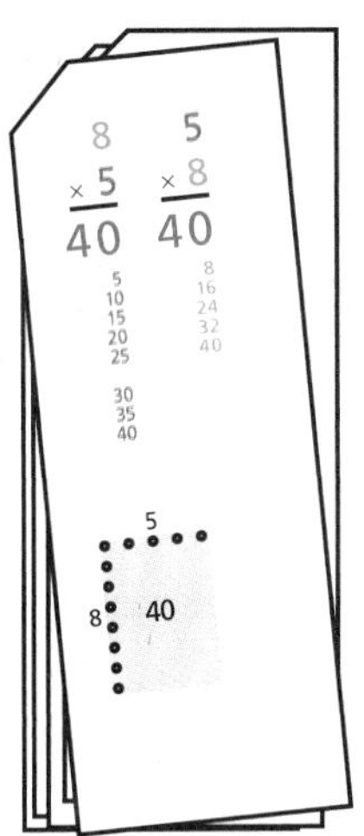

1. Each player looks through the cards and writes any nine of the products in the squares of a Game Grid. A player may write the same product more than once.
2. Shuffle the cards and place them exercise side up in the center of the table.
3. Players take turns. On each turn, a player finds the answer to the multiplication on the top card and then turns the card over to check the answer.
4. If the answer is correct, the player looks to see if the product is on the game grid. If it is, the player puts an X through that grid square. If the answer is wrong, or if the product is not on the grid, the player does not mark anything. The player then puts the card problem side up on the bottom of the stack.
5. The first player to mark three squares in a row (horizontally, vertically, or diagonally) wins.

~~40~~	32	56
72	16	~~24~~
64	42	56

PATH to FLUENCY Play *Division Race*

Read the rules for playing *Division Race*. Then play the game with a partner.

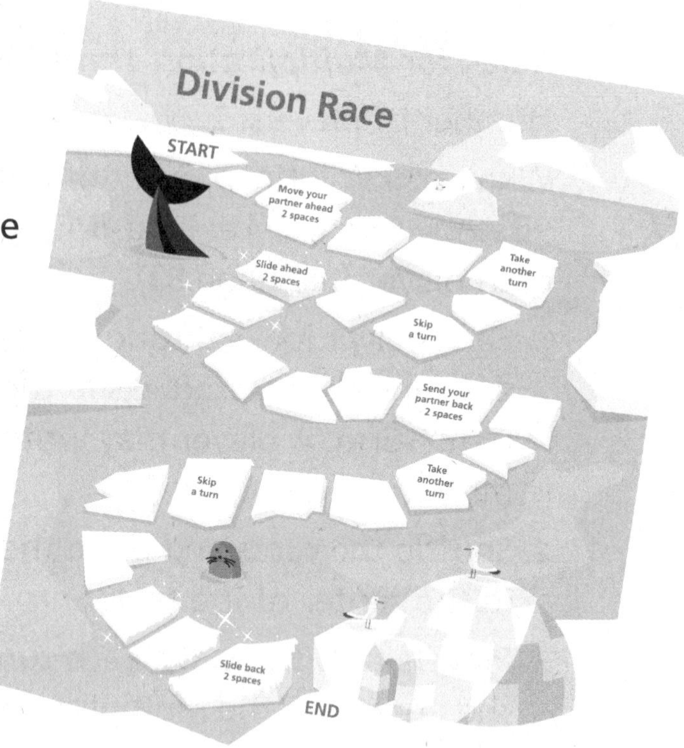

Rules for *Division Race*

Number of players: 2

What You Will Need: a set of Division Strategy Cards, the *Division Race* game board (see page 84), a different game piece for each player

1. Shuffle the cards and then place them exercise side up on the table.
2. Both players put their game pieces on "START."
3. Players take turns. On each turn, a player finds the answer to the division on the top card and then turns the card over to check the answer.
4. If the answer is correct, the player moves *forward* that number of spaces. If a player's answer is wrong, the player moves *back* a number of spaces equal to the correct answer. Players cannot move back beyond the "START" square. The player puts the card on the bottom of the stack.
5. If a player lands on a space with special instructions, he or she should follow those instructions.
6. The game ends when everyone lands on or passes the "End" square.

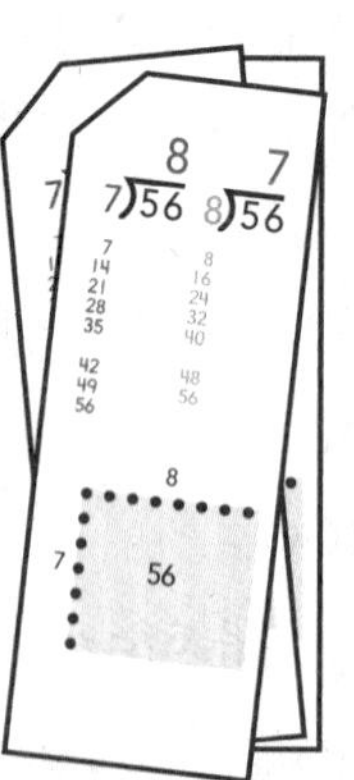

Name ____________________

Division Race

Name ___________________

PATH to FLUENCY **Dashes 1–4**

Complete each Dash. Check your answers on page 89.

Dash 1 2s and 5s Multiplications	Dash 2 2s and 5s Divisions	Dash 3 9s and 10s Multiplications	Dash 4 9s and 10s Divisions
a. 2 × 6 = ___	a. 18 / 2 = ___	a. 9 × 10 = ___	a. 100 / 10 = ___
b. 9 * 5 = ___	b. 25 ÷ 5 = ___	b. 10 * 3 = ___	b. 9 ÷ 9 = ___
c. 7 • 2 = ___	c. 8 / 2 = ___	c. 1 • 9 = ___	c. 30 / 10 = ___
d. 5 × 8 = ___	d. 45 ÷ 5 = ___	d. 2 × 10 = ___	d. 81 ÷ 9 = ___
e. 2 * 4 = ___	e. 16 / 2 = ___	e. 9 * 9 = ___	e. 70 / 10 = ___
f. 3 • 5 = ___	f. 20 ÷ 5 = ___	f. 10 • 6 = ___	f. 45 ÷ 9 = ___
g. 1 × 2 = ___	g. 4 / 2 = ___	g. 4 × 9 = ___	g. 10 / 10 = ___
h. 5 * 7 = ___	h. 40 ÷ 5 = ___	h. 10 × 10 = ___	h. 54 ÷ 9 = ___
i. 2 • 9 = ___	i. 20 / 2 = ___	i. 9 * 2 = ___	i. 50 / 10 = ___
j. 4 × 5 = ___	j. 35 ÷ 5 = ___	j. 1 • 10 = ___	j. 27 ÷ 9 = ___
k. 5 * 2 = ___	k. 6 / 2 = ___	k. 7 × 9 = ___	k. 20 / 10 = ___
l. 5 • 1 = ___	l. 15 ÷ 5 = ___	l. 10 * 5 = ___	l. 72 ÷ 9 = ___
m. 2 × 2 = ___	m. 14 / 2 = ___	m. 9 • 8 = ___	m. 40 / 10 = ___
n. 10 × 5 = ___	n. 5 ÷ 5 = ___	n. 7 × 10 = ___	n. 18 ÷ 9 = ___
o. 10 * 2 = ___	o. 10 / 2 = ___	o. 3 * 9 = ___	o. 60 / 10 = ___
p. 5 • 6 = ___	p. 10 ÷ 5 = ___	p. 10 • 4 = ___	p. 90 ÷ 9 = ___
q. 2 × 3 = ___	q. 6 / 2 = ___	q. 9 × 5 = ___	q. 90 / 10 = ___
r. 5 * 5 = ___	r. 30 ÷ 5 = ___	r. 8 * 10 = ___	r. 63 ÷ 9 = ___
s. 8 • 2 = ___	s. 2 / 2 = ___	s. 6 • 9 = ___	s. 80 / 10 = ___
t. 6 × 5 = ___	t. 45 ÷ 5 = ___	t. 10 × 9 = ___	t. 36 ÷ 9 = ___

PATH to FLUENCY

Dashes 5–8

Complete each Dash. Check your answers on page 89.

Dash 5 3s and 4s Multiplications
a. 3 × 9 = ___
b. 4 * 2 = ___
c. 6 • 3 = ___
d. 10 × 4 = ___
e. 3 * 1 = ___
f. 4 • 1 = ___
g. 10 × 3 = ___
h. 5 * 4 = ___
i. 3 • 3 = ___
j. 4 × 4 = ___
k. 8 * 3 = ___
l. 7 • 4 = ___
m. 3 × 2 = ___
n. 4 * 9 = ___
o. 7 • 3 = ___
p. 3 × 4 = ___
q. 3 * 5 = ___
r. 4 • 6 = ___
s. 4 × 3 = ___
t. 8 * 4 = ___

Dash 6 3s and 4s Divisions
a. 12 / 4 = ___
b. 20 ÷ 4 = ___
c. 21 / 3 = ___
d. 16 ÷ 4 = ___
e. 9 / 3 = ___
f. 32 ÷ 4 = ___
g. 24 / 4 = ___
h. 18 ÷ 3 = ___
i. 40 / 4 = ___
j. 12 ÷ 3 = ___
k. 6 / 3 = ___
l. 28 ÷ 4 = ___
m. 24 / 3 = ___
n. 20 ÷ 4 = ___
o. 27 / 3 = ___
p. 15 ÷ 3 = ___
q. 27 / 3 = ___
r. 36 ÷ 4 = ___
s. 8 / 4 = ___
t. 40 ÷ 4 = ___

Dash 7 0s and 1s Multiplications
a. 0 × 6 = ___
b. 1 * 4 = ___
c. 4 • 0 = ___
d. 8 × 1 = ___
e. 0 * 2 = ___
f. 1 • 3 = ___
g. 9 × 0 = ___
h. 2 * 1 = ___
i. 0 • 8 = ___
j. 1 × 10 = ___
k. 7 * 0 = ___
l. 1 • 1 = ___
m. 0 × 0 = ___
n. 5 * 1 = ___
o. 1 • 0 = ___
p. 1 × 6 = ___
q. 5 * 0 = ___
r. 0 • 3 = ___
s. 7 × 1 = ___
t. 1 * 9 = ___

Dash 8 1s and *n* ÷ *n* Divisions
a. 9 / 9 = ___
b. 8 ÷ 1 = ___
c. 7 / 7 = ___
d. 6 ÷ 1 = ___
e. 1 / 1 = ___
f. 4 ÷ 1 = ___
g. 2 / 2 = ___
h. 2 ÷ 1 = ___
i. 8 / 8 = ___
j. 9 ÷ 1 = ___
k. 3 / 3 = ___
l. 5 ÷ 1 = ___
m. 5 / 5 = ___
n. 10 / 10 = ___
o. 7 ÷ 1 = ___
p. 4 / 4 = ___
q. 10 ÷ 1 = ___
r. 6 / 6 = ___
s. 3 ÷ 1 = ___
t. 1 / 1 = ___

Name ______

PATH to FLUENCY

Dashes 9–12

Complete each Dash. Check your answers on page 90.

Dash 9 2s, 5s, 9s, 10s Multiplications	Dash 10 2s, 5s, 9s, 10s Divisions	Dash 11 3s, 4s, 0s, 1s Multiplications	Dash 12 3s, 4s, 1s Divisions
a. 4 × 5 = ___	a. 8 / 2 = ___	a. 3 × 0 = ___	a. 12 / 4 = ___
b. 10 • 3 = ___	b. 50 ÷ 10 = ___	b. 4 • 6 = ___	b. 5 ÷ 1 = ___
c. 8 * 9 = ___	c. 15 / 5 = ___	c. 9 * 1 = ___	c. 21 / 3 = ___
d. 6 × 2 = ___	d. 63 ÷ 9 = ___	d. 3 × 3 = ___	d. 1 ÷ 1 = ___
e. 5 • 7 = ___	e. 90 / 10 = ___	e. 8 • 4 = ___	e. 16 / 4 = ___
f. 10 * 5 = ___	f. 90 ÷ 9 = ___	f. 0 * 5 = ___	f. 9 ÷ 3 = ___
g. 8 × 2 = ___	g. 35 / 5 = ___	g. 1 × 6 = ___	g. 32 / 4 = ___
h. 6 • 10 = ___	h. 14 ÷ 2 = ___	h. 4 • 3 = ___	h. 8 ÷ 1 = ___
i. 9 * 3 = ___	i. 27 / 9 = ___	i. 7 * 4 = ___	i. 24 / 4 = ___
j. 2 × 9 = ___	j. 45 / 5 = ___	j. 3 × 7 = ___	j. 18 / 3 = ___
k. 5 • 8 = ___	k. 10 ÷ 10 = ___	k. 0 • 1 = ___	k. 10 ÷ 1 = ___
l. 10 * 7 = ___	l. 25 / 5 = ___	l. 10 * 1 = ___	l. 40 / 4 = ___
m. 5 × 5 = ___	m. 54 ÷ 9 = ___	m. 4 × 4 = ___	m. 12 ÷ 3 = ___
n. 1 • 5 = ___	n. 6 / 2 = ___	n. 9 • 3 = ___	n. 6 / 3 = ___
o. 9 * 6 = ___	o. 72 ÷ 9 = ___	o. 8 * 0 = ___	o. 4 ÷ 4 = ___
p. 10 × 10 = ___	p. 40 / 5 = ___	p. 5 × 4 = ___	p. 7 / 1 = ___
q. 4 • 2 = ___	q. 80 ÷ 10 = ___	q. 1 • 6 = ___	q. 28 ÷ 4 = ___
r. 10 * 8 = ___	r. 18 ÷ 2 = ___	r. 3 * 8 = ___	r. 24 ÷ 3 = ___
s. 3 × 9 = ___	s. 36 / 9 = ___	s. 4 × 9 = ___	s. 20 / 4 = ___
t. 9 • 9 = ___	t. 30 ÷ 5 = ___	t. 0 • 4 = ___	t. 27 ÷ 3 = ___

PATH to FLUENCY

Dashes 9A–12A

Complete each Dash. Check your answers on page 90.

Dash 9A 2s, 5s, 9s, 10s Multiplications	Dash 10A 2s, 5s, 9s, 10s Divisions	Dash 11A 3s, 4s, 0s, 1s Multiplications	Dash 12A 3s, 4s, 1s Divisions
a. 9 × 9 = ____	a. 30 / 5 = ____	a. 0 × 4 = ____	a. 10 / 1 = ____
b. 4 * 5 = ____	b. 18 ÷ 2 = ____	b. 4 * 9 = ____	b. 40 ÷ 4 = ____
c. 10 • 3 = ____	c. 40 / 5 = ____	c. 3 • 8 = ____	c. 12 / 3 = ____
d. 3 × 9 = ____	d. 6 ÷ 2 = ____	d. 3 × 0 = ____	d. 6 ÷ 3 = ____
e. 10 * 8 = ____	e. 25 / 5 = ____	e. 4 * 6 = ____	e. 4 / 4 = ____
f. 6 • 2 = ____	f. 45 ÷ 5 = ____	f. 9 • 1 = ____	f. 7 ÷ 1 = ____
g. 8 × 9 = ____	g. 14 / 2 = ____	g. 3 × 3 = ____	g. 28 / 4 = ____
h. 4 * 2 = ____	h. 90 ÷ 9 = ____	h. 8 * 4 = ____	h. 24 ÷ 3 = ____
i. 10 • 10 = ____	i. 63 / 9 = ____	i. 0 • 5 = ____	i. 20 / 4 = ____
j. 9 × 6 = ____	j. 50 ÷ 10 = ____	j. 1 × 6 = ____	j. 27 ÷ 3 = ____
k. 5 * 7 = ____	k. 8 / 2 = ____	k. 5 * 4 = ____	k. 12 / 4 = ____
l. 10 • 5 = ____	l. 15 ÷ 5 = ____	l. 8 • 0 = ____	l. 5 ÷ 1 = ____
m. 8 × 2 = ____	m. 90 / 10 = ____	m. 9 × 3 = ____	m. 21 / 3 = ____
n. 6 * 10 = ____	n. 35 ÷ 5 = ____	n. 4 * 4 = ____	n. 1 ÷ 1 = ____
o. 2 * 9 = ____	o. 27 / 9 = ____	o. 10 • 1 = ____	o. 16 / 4 = ____
p. 9 • 6 = ____	p. 10 ÷ 10 = ____	p. 4 × 3 = ____	p. 9 ÷ 3 = ____
q. 1 × 5 = ____	q. 54 / 9 = ____	q. 7 * 4 = ____	q. 32 / 4 = ____
r. 5 * 5 = ____	r. 72 ÷ 9 = ____	r. 3 • 7 = ____	r. 8 ÷ 1 = ____
s. 10 • 7 = ____	s. 80 / 10 = ____	s. 0 × 1 = ____	s. 24 / 4 = ____
t. 5 × 8 = ____	t. 36 ÷ 9 = ____	t. 10 * 1 = ____	t. 18 ÷ 3 = ____

Name

PATH to FLUENCY

Answers to Dashes 1–8

Use this sheet to check your answers to the Dashes on pages 85 and 86.

Dash 1 2s and 5s ×	Dash 2 2s and 5s ÷	Dash 3 9s and 10s ×	Dash 4 9s and 10s ÷	Dash 5 3s and 4s ×	Dash 6 3s and 4s ÷	Dash 7 0s and 1s ×	Dash 8 1s and $n \div n$ ÷
a. 12	a. 9	a. 90	a. 10	a. 27	a. 3	a. 0	a. 1
b. 45	b. 5	b. 30	b. 1	b. 8	b. 5	b. 4	b. 8
c. 14	c. 4	c. 9	c. 3	c. 18	c. 7	c. 0	c. 1
d. 40	d. 9	d. 20	d. 9	d. 40	d. 4	d. 8	d. 6
e. 8	e. 8	e. 81	e. 7	e. 3	e. 3	e. 0	e. 1
f. 15	f. 4	f. 60	f. 5	f. 4	f. 8	f. 3	f. 4
g. 2	g. 2	g. 36	g. 1	g. 30	g. 6	g. 0	g. 1
h. 35	h. 8	h. 100	h. 6	h. 20	h. 6	h. 2	h. 2
i. 18	i. 10	i. 18	i. 5	i. 9	i. 10	i. 0	i. 1
j. 20	j. 7	j. 10	j. 3	j. 16	j. 4	j. 10	j. 9
k. 10	k. 3	k. 63	k. 2	k. 24	k. 2	k. 0	k. 1
l. 5	l. 3	l. 50	l. 8	l. 28	l. 7	l. 1	l. 5
m. 4	m. 7	m. 72	m. 4	m. 6	m. 8	m. 0	m. 1
n. 50	n. 1	n. 70	n. 2	n. 36	n. 5	n. 5	n. 1
o. 20	o. 5	o. 27	o. 6	o. 21	o. 9	o. 0	o. 7
p. 30	p. 2	p. 40	p. 10	p. 12	p. 5	p. 6	p. 1
q. 6	q. 3	q. 45	q. 9	q. 15	q. 9	q. 0	q. 10
r. 25	r. 6	r. 80	r. 7	r. 24	r. 9	r. 0	r. 1
s. 16	s. 1	s. 54	s. 8	s. 12	s. 2	s. 7	s. 3
t. 30	t. 9	t. 90	t. 4	t. 32	t. 10	t. 9	t. 1

PATH to FLUENCY Answers to Dashes 9–12, 9A–12A

Use this sheet to check your answers to the Dashes on pages 87 and 88.

Dash 9 ×	Dash 10 ÷	Dash 11 ×	Dash 12 ÷	Dash 9A ×	Dash 10A ÷	Dash 11A ×	Dash 12A ÷
a. 20	a. 4	a. 0	a. 3	a. 81	a. 6	a. 0	a. 10
b. 30	b. 5	b. 24	b. 5	b. 20	b. 9	b. 36	b. 10
c. 72	c. 3	c. 9	c. 7	c. 30	c. 8	c. 24	c. 4
d. 12	d. 7	d. 9	d. 1	d. 27	d. 3	d. 0	d. 2
e. 35	e. 9	e. 32	e. 4	e. 80	e. 5	e. 24	e. 1
f. 50	f. 10	f. 0	f. 3	f. 12	f. 9	f. 9	f. 7
g. 16	g. 7	g. 6	g. 8	g. 72	g. 7	g. 9	g. 7
h. 60	h. 7	h. 12	h. 8	h. 8	h. 10	h. 32	h. 8
i. 27	i. 3	i. 28	i. 6	i. 100	i. 7	i. 0	i. 5
j. 18	j. 9	j. 21	j. 6	j. 54	j. 5	j. 6	j. 9
k. 40	k. 1	k. 0	k. 10	k. 35	k. 4	k. 20	k. 3
l. 70	l. 5	l. 10	l. 10	l. 50	l. 3	l. 0	l. 5
m. 25	m. 6	m. 16	m. 4	m. 16	m. 9	m. 27	m. 7
n. 5	n. 3	n. 27	n. 2	n. 60	n. 7	n. 16	n. 1
o. 54	o. 8	o. 0	o. 1	o. 18	o. 3	o. 10	o. 4
p. 100	p. 8	p. 20	p. 7	p. 54	p. 1	p. 12	p. 3
q. 8	q. 8	q. 6	q. 7	q. 5	q. 6	q. 28	q. 8
r. 80	r. 9	r. 24	r. 8	r. 25	r. 8	r. 21	r. 8
s. 27	s. 4	s. 36	s. 5	s. 70	s. 8	s. 0	s. 6
t. 81	t. 6	t. 0	t. 9	t. 40	t. 4	t. 10	t. 6

Name ______________________________

Solve Word Problems with 2s, 3s, 4s, 5s, and 9s

Write an equation and solve the problem.

Show your work.

1. Toni counted 36 chairs in the restaurant. Each table had 4 chairs. How many tables were there?

____

2. One wall of an art gallery has 5 rows of paintings. Each row has row of 9 paintings. How many paintings are on the wall?

____

3. Josh's muffin pan is an array with 4 rows and 6 columns. How many muffins can Josh make in the pan?

____

4. To get ready for the school spelling bee, Tanya studied 3 hours each night for an entire week. How many hours did she study?

____

5. The 14 trumpet players in the marching band lined up in 2 equal rows. How many trumpet players were in each row?

____

6. The Sunnyside Riding Stable has 9 horses. The owners are going to buy new horseshoes for all the horses. How many horseshoes are needed?

____

Make Sense of Problems

Write an equation and solve the problem.

Show your work.

7. Sadie plans to read 2 books every month for 6 months. How many books will she read during that time?

8. A farmer sells pumpkins for \$5 each. On Friday the farmer made \$35 from the sale of pumpkins. How many pumpkins did the farmer sell on Friday?

9. Each student collected 10 leaves for a group science project. If the group collected a total of 80 leaves, how many students are in the group?

Write a Word Problem

10. Write and solve a word problem that can be solved using the equation $4 \times 1 = n$.

Check Understanding

Write a related multiplication or division equation for the equation you wrote for Problem 9.

Name ______________________________

PATH to FLUENCY

Math and Hobbies

A hobby is something you do for fun. Owen's hobby is photography. He took pictures and displayed them on a poster.

Solve.

1. How many photos did Owen display on the poster? Explain the different strategies you can use to find the answer. Write an equation for each.

____

____

____

____

2. What other ways could Owen have arranged the photos in an array on a poster?

____

____

PATH to FLUENCY What is Your Hobby?

Carina asked some third graders, "What is your hobby?" The answers are shown under the photos.

Dancing
Four third graders said dancing.

Photography
Eight more than dancing said photography.

Reading
Six less than photography said reading.

Games
Eight third graders said games.

3 **Use the information above to complete the chart below.**

What is Your Hobby?	
Hobby	Number of Students
Dancing	
Photography	
Games	
Reading	

4 **Use the chart to complete the pictograph below.**

Hobbies	
Dancing	
Photography	
Games	
Reading	

Each ☐ stands for 2 third graders.

5 How many third graders answered Carina's question?

____

expression

Order of Operations

square number

A combination of numbers, variables, and/or operation signs. An expression does not have an equal sign.

Examples:

$4 + 7$ $a - 3$

A set of rules that state the order in which the operations in an expression should be done.

STEP 1: Perform operations inside parentheses first.

STEP 2: Multiply and divide from left to right.

STEP 3: Add and subtract from left to right.

The product of a whole number and itself.

Example:

$3 \times 3 = 9$

↑

square number

Name

PATH to FLUENCY

Explore Patterns with 6s

What patterns do you see below?

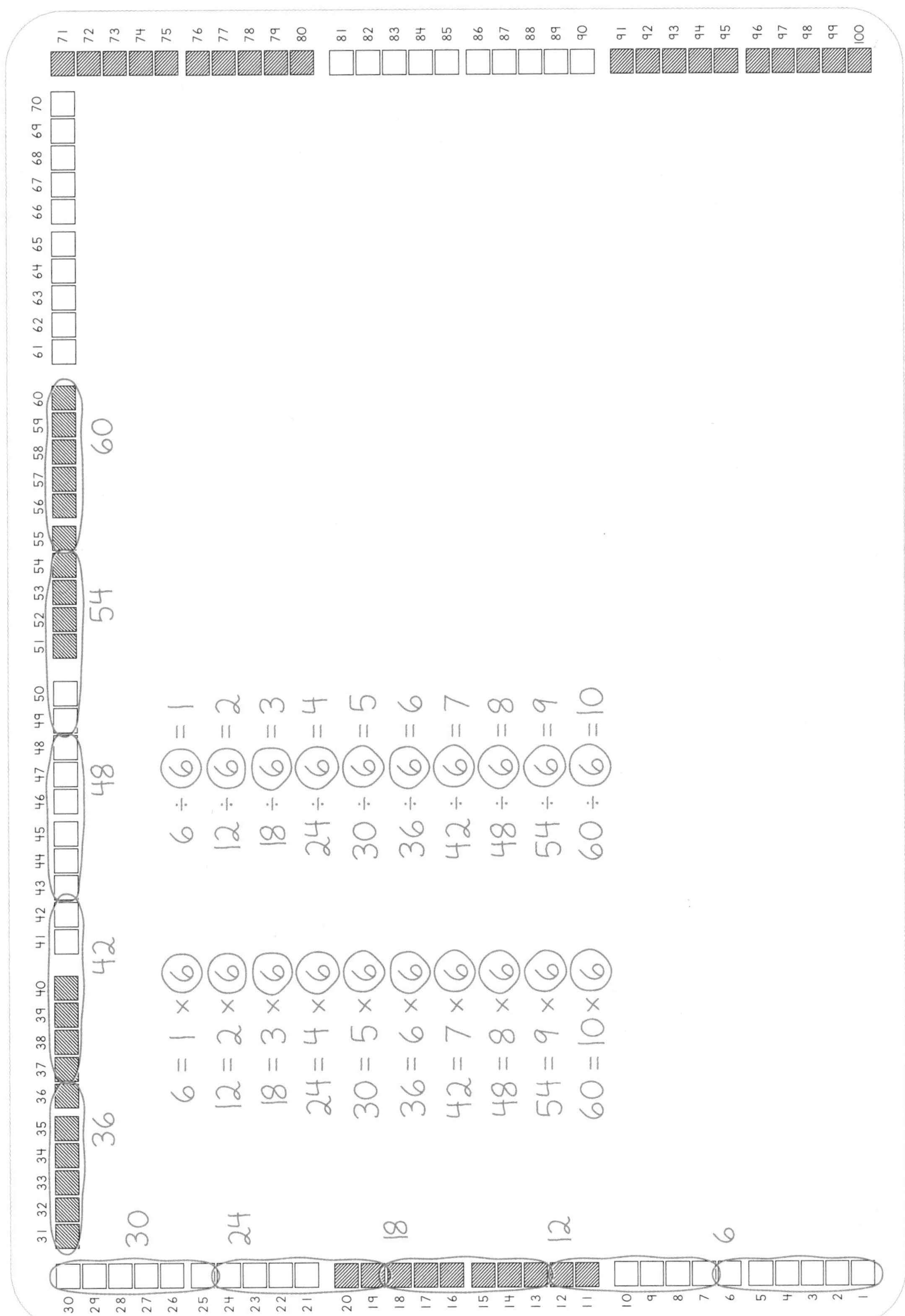

PATH to FLUENCY Strategies for Multiplying with 6

You can use 6s multiplications that you know to find 6s multiplications that you don't know. Here are some strategies for 6×6.

- **Strategy 1:** Start with 5×6, and count by 6 from there.
  $5 \times 6 = 30$, the next count-by is 36. So, $6 \times 6 = 36$.
- **Strategy 2:** Double a 3s multiplication.
  6×6 is twice 6×3, which is 18. So, $6 \times 6 = 18 + 18 = 36$.
- **Strategy 3:** Combine two multiplications you know.

$4 \times 6 = 24$	4 sixes are 24.
$2 \times 6 = 12$	2 sixes are 12.
$6 \times 6 = 36$	6 sixes are 36.

Here are two ways to show Strategy 3 with drawings.

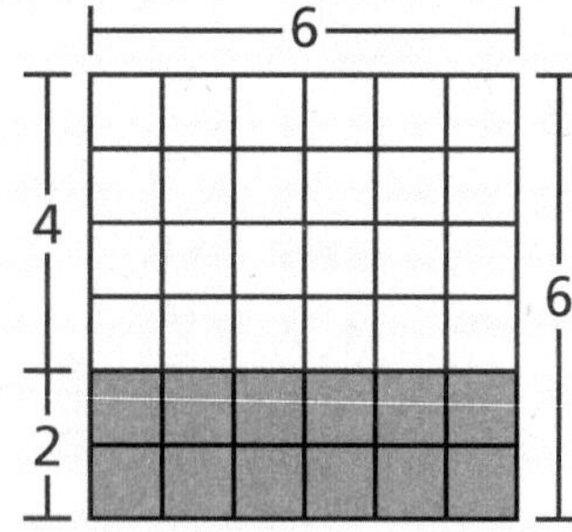

unshaded area: $4 \times 6 = 24$
shaded area: $2 \times 6 = 12$
total area: $6 \times 6 = 36$

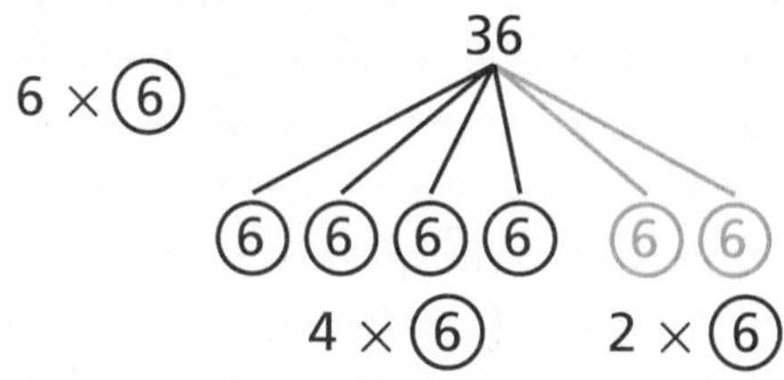

Explanation:
6 groups of 6 is
4 groups of 6 plus
2 groups of 6.

- **Strategy 4:** Add 6 on to the 6s multiplication before or subtract 6 from the multiplication ahead.
  $5 \times 6 = 30$, add 6 more to get 36. So, $6 \times 6 = 36$.

Apply Strategies for 6s Multiplications

Use any of the strategies above.

1. $7 \times 6 =$ ______
2. $8 \times 6 =$ ______
3. $9 \times 6 =$ ______

Check Understanding

Describe the strategy you used to find 8×6.

Name

Study Sheet C

6s		
Count-bys	**Mixed Up ×**	**Mixed Up ÷**
1 × 6 = 6	10 × 6 = 60	54 ÷ 6 = 9
2 × 6 = 12	8 × 6 = 48	30 ÷ 6 = 5
3 × 6 = 18	2 × 6 = 12	12 ÷ 6 = 2
4 × 6 = 24	6 × 6 = 36	60 ÷ 6 = 10
5 × 6 = 30	4 × 6 = 24	48 ÷ 6 = 8
6 × 6 = 36	1 × 6 = 6	36 ÷ 6 = 6
7 × 6 = 42	9 × 6 = 54	6 ÷ 6 = 1
8 × 6 = 48	3 × 6 = 18	42 ÷ 6 = 7
9 × 6 = 54	7 × 6 = 42	18 ÷ 6 = 3
10 × 6 = 60	5 × 6 = 30	24 ÷ 6 = 4

7s		
Count-bys	**Mixed Up ×**	**Mixed Up ÷**
1 × 7 = 7	6 × 7 = 42	70 ÷ 7 = 10
2 × 7 = 14	8 × 7 = 56	14 ÷ 7 = 2
3 × 7 = 21	5 × 7 = 35	28 ÷ 7 = 4
4 × 7 = 28	9 × 7 = 63	56 ÷ 7 = 8
5 × 7 = 35	4 × 7 = 28	42 ÷ 7 = 6
6 × 7 = 42	10 × 7 = 70	63 ÷ 7 = 9
7 × 7 = 49	3 × 7 = 21	21 ÷ 7 = 3
8 × 7 = 56	1 × 7 = 7	49 ÷ 7 = 7
9 × 7 = 63	7 × 7 = 49	7 ÷ 7 = 1
10 × 7 = 70	2 × 7 = 14	35 ÷ 7 = 5

8s		
Count-bys	**Mixed Up ×**	**Mixed Up ÷**
1 × 8 = 8	6 × 8 = 48	16 ÷ 8 = 2
2 × 8 = 16	10 × 8 = 80	40 ÷ 8 = 5
3 × 8 = 24	7 × 8 = 56	72 ÷ 8 = 9
4 × 8 = 32	2 × 8 = 16	32 ÷ 8 = 4
5 × 8 = 40	4 × 8 = 32	8 ÷ 8 = 1
6 × 8 = 48	8 × 8 = 64	80 ÷ 8 = 10
7 × 8 = 56	5 × 8 = 40	64 ÷ 8 = 8
8 × 8 = 64	9 × 8 = 72	24 ÷ 8 = 3
9 × 8 = 72	3 × 8 = 24	56 ÷ 8 = 7
10 × 8 = 80	1 × 8 = 8	48 ÷ 8 = 6

Squares		
Count-bys	**Mixed Up ×**	**Mixed Up ÷**
1 × 1 = 1	3 × 3 = 9	25 ÷ 5 = 5
2 × 2 = 4	9 × 9 = 81	4 ÷ 2 = 2
3 × 3 = 9	4 × 4 = 16	81 ÷ 9 = 9
4 × 4 = 16	6 × 6 = 36	9 ÷ 3 = 3
5 × 5 = 25	2 × 2 = 4	36 ÷ 6 = 6
6 × 6 = 36	7 × 7 = 49	100 ÷ 10 = 10
7 × 7 = 49	10 × 10 = 100	16 ÷ 4 = 4
8 × 8 = 64	1 × 1 = 1	49 ÷ 7 = 7
9 × 9 = 81	5 × 5 = 25	1 ÷ 1 = 1
10 × 10 = 100	8 × 8 = 64	64 ÷ 8 = 8

Name ______________________________

PATH to FLUENCY

Check Sheet 7: 6s and 8s

6s Multiplications	6s Divisions	8s Multiplications	8s Divisions
10 × 6 = 60	24 / 6 = 4	2 × 8 = 16	72 / 8 = 9
6 • 4 = 24	48 ÷ 6 = 8	8 • 10 = 80	16 ÷ 8 = 2
6 * 7 = 42	60 / 6 = 10	3 * 8 = 24	40 / 8 = 5
2 × 6 = 12	12 ÷ 6 = 2	9 × 8 = 72	8 ÷ 8 = 1
6 • 5 = 30	42 / 6 = 7	8 • 4 = 32	80 / 8 = 10
6 * 8 = 48	30 ÷ 6 = 5	8 * 7 = 56	48 ÷ 8 = 6
9 × 6 = 54	6 / 6 = 1	5 × 8 = 40	56 / 8 = 7
6 • 1 = 6	18 ÷ 6 = 3	8 • 6 = 48	24 ÷ 8 = 3
6 * 6 = 36	54 / 6 = 9	1 * 8 = 8	64 / 8 = 8
6 × 3 = 18	36 / 6 = 6	8 × 8 = 64	32 / 8 = 4
6 • 6 = 36	48 ÷ 6 = 8	4 • 8 = 32	80 ÷ 8 = 10
5 * 6 = 30	12 / 6 = 2	6 * 8 = 48	56 / 8 = 7
6 × 2 = 12	24 ÷ 6 = 4	8 × 3 = 24	8 ÷ 8 = 1
4 • 6 = 24	60 / 6 = 10	7 • 8 = 56	24 / 8 = 3
6 * 9 = 54	6 ÷ 6 = 1	8 * 2 = 16	64 ÷ 8 = 8
8 × 6 = 48	42 / 6 = 7	8 × 9 = 72	16 / 8 = 2
7 • 6 = 42	18 ÷ 6 = 3	8 • 1 = 8	72 ÷ 8 = 9
6 * 10 = 60	36 ÷ 6 = 6	8 * 8 = 64	32 ÷ 8 = 4
1 × 6 = 6	30 / 6 = 5	10 × 8 = 80	40 / 8 = 5
4 • 6 = 24	54 ÷ 6 = 9	5 • 8 = 40	48 ÷ 8 = 6

Name ____________________

PATH to FLUENCY

Explore Patterns with 7s

What patterns do you see below?

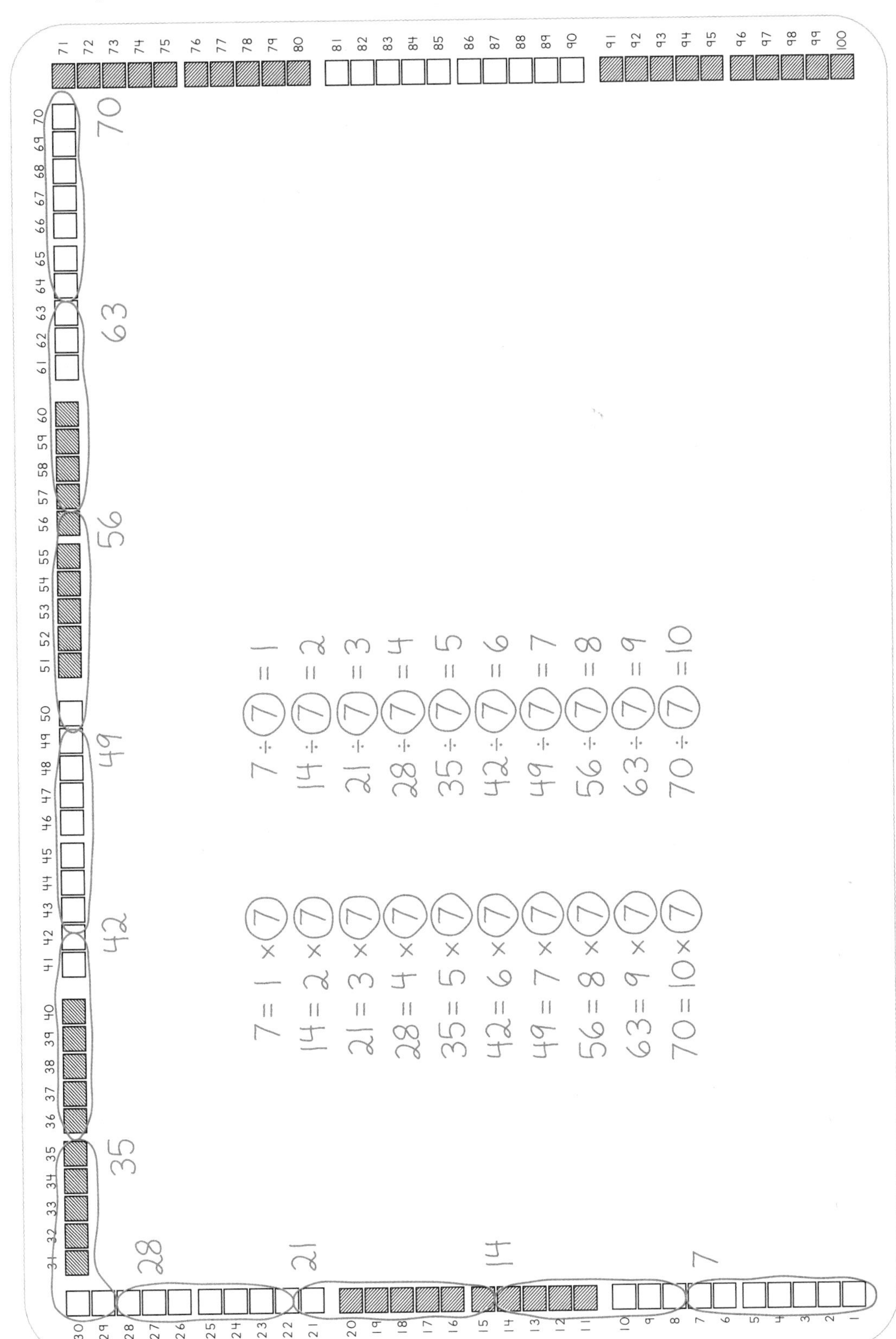

PATH to FLUENCY More Fast Array Drawings

Find the unknown number for each fast array drawing.

1 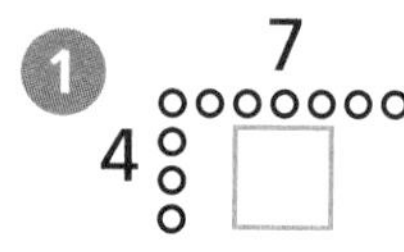
7
4 □

2 7
□ 42

3 5
6 □

4 □
3 24

5 8
6 □

6 5
□ 10

7 6
□ 36

8 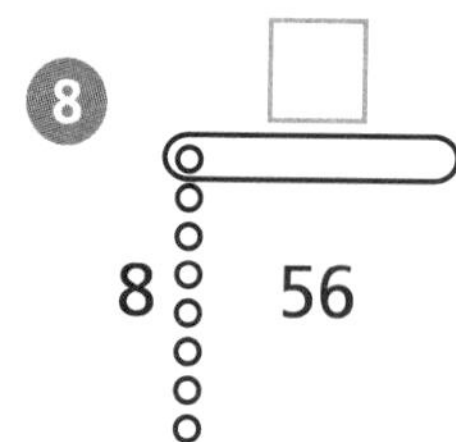
□
8 56

9 4
3 □

10 □
7 49

11 5
□ 35

12 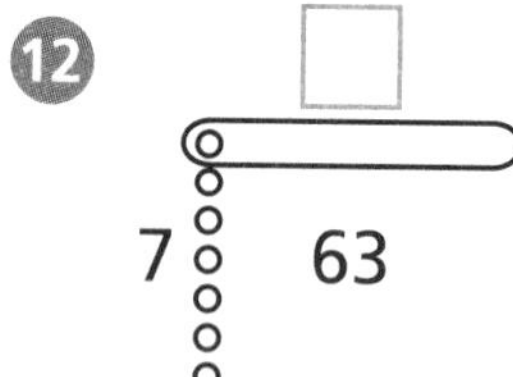
□
7 63

13 6
8 □

14 4
□ 24

15 □
9 54

Check Understanding

Draw a fast array drawing to find $49 \div 7$.

Name ____________________

PATH to FLUENCY

Check Sheet 8: 7s and Squares

7s Multiplications	7s Divisions	Squares Multiplications	Squares Divisions
4 × 7 = 28	14 / 7 = 2	8 × 8 = 64	81 / 9 = 9
7 • 2 = 14	28 ÷ 7 = 4	10 • 10 = 100	4 ÷ 2 = 2
7 * 8 = 56	70 / 7 = 10	3 * 3 = 9	25 / 5 = 5
7 × 7 = 49	56 ÷ 7 = 8	9 × 9 = 81	1 ÷ 1 = 1
7 • 1 = 7	42 / 7 = 6	4 • 4 = 16	100 / 10 = 10
7 * 10 = 70	63 ÷ 7 = 9	7 * 7 = 49	36 ÷ 6 = 6
3 × 7 = 21	7 / 7 = 1	5 × 5 = 25	49 / 7 = 7
7 • 6 = 42	49 ÷ 7 = 7	6 • 6 = 36	9 ÷ 3 = 3
5 * 7 = 35	21 / 7 = 3	1 * 1 = 1	64 / 8 = 8
7 × 9 = 63	35 / 7 = 5	5 * 5 = 25	16 / 4 = 4
7 • 4 = 28	7 ÷ 7 = 1	1 • 1 = 1	100 ÷ 10 = 10
9 * 7 = 63	63 / 7 = 9	3 • 3 = 9	49 / 7 = 7
2 × 7 = 14	14 ÷ 7 = 2	10 × 10 = 100	1 ÷ 1 = 1
7 • 5 = 35	70 / 7 = 10	4 × 4 = 16	9 / 3 = 3
8 * 7 = 56	21 ÷ 7 = 3	9 * 9 = 81	64 ÷ 8 = 8
7 × 3 = 21	49 / 7 = 7	2 × 2 = 4	4 / 2 = 2
6 • 7 = 42	28 ÷ 7 = 4	6 * 6 = 36	81 ÷ 9 = 9
10 * 7 = 70	56 ÷ 7 = 8	7 × 7 = 49	16 ÷ 4 = 4
1 × 7 = 7	35 / 7 = 5	5 • 5 = 25	25 / 5 = 5
7 • 7 = 49	42 ÷ 7 = 6	8 • 8 = 64	36 ÷ 6 = 6

Name ______________________

PATH to FLUENCY

Check Sheet 9: 6s, 7s, and 8s

6s, 7s, and 8s Multiplications	6s, 7s, and 8s Multiplications	6s, 7s, and 8s Divisions	6s, 7s, and 8s Divisions
1 × 6 = 6	0 × 8 = 0	24 / 6 = 4	54 / 6 = 9
6 • 7 = 42	6 • 2 = 12	21 ÷ 7 = 3	24 ÷ 8 = 3
3 * 8 = 24	4 * 7 = 28	16 / 8 = 2	14 / 7 = 2
6 × 2 = 12	8 × 3 = 24	24 ÷ 8 = 3	32 ÷ 8 = 4
7 • 5 = 35	5 • 6 = 30	14 / 7 = 2	18 / 6 = 3
8 * 4 = 32	7 * 2 = 14	30 ÷ 6 = 5	56 ÷ 7 = 8
6 × 6 = 36	3 × 8 = 24	35 / 7 = 5	40 / 8 = 5
8 • 7 = 56	6 • 4 = 24	24 ÷ 8 = 3	35 ÷ 7 = 5
9 * 8 = 72	0 * 7 = 0	18 / 6 = 3	12 / 6 = 2
6 × 10 = 60	8 × 1 = 8	12 / 6 = 2	21 / 7 = 3
7 • 1 = 7	8 • 6 = 48	42 ÷ 7 = 6	16 ÷ 8 = 2
8 * 3 = 24	7 * 9 = 63	56 / 8 = 7	42 / 6 = 7
5 × 6 = 30	10 × 8 = 80	49 ÷ 7 = 7	80 ÷ 8 = 10
4 • 7 = 28	6 • 10 = 60	16 / 8 = 2	36 / 6 = 6
2 * 8 = 16	3 * 7 = 21	60 ÷ 6 = 10	7 ÷ 7 = 1
7 × 7 = 49	8 × 4 = 32	54 / 6 = 9	64 / 8 = 8
7 • 6 = 42	6 • 5 = 30	8 ÷ 8 = 1	24 ÷ 6 = 4
8 * 8 = 64	7 * 4 = 28	28 ÷ 7 = 4	21 ÷ 7 = 3
9 × 6 = 54	8 × 8 = 64	72 / 8 = 9	49 / 7 = 7
10 • 7 = 70	6 • 9 = 54	56 ÷ 7 = 8	24 ÷ 8 = 3

PATH to FLUENCY Check Sheet 10: 0s–10s

0s–10s Multiplications	0s–10s Multiplications	0s–10s Divisions	0s–10s Divisions
9 × 0 = 0	9 × 4 = 36	9 / 1 = 9	90 / 10 = 9
1 • 1 = 1	5 • 9 = 45	12 ÷ 3 = 4	64 ÷ 8 = 8
2 * 3 = 6	6 * 10 = 60	14 / 2 = 7	15 / 5 = 3
1 × 3 = 3	7 × 3 = 21	20 ÷ 4 = 5	12 ÷ 6 = 2
5 • 4 = 20	5 • 3 = 15	10 / 5 = 2	14 / 7 = 2
7 * 5 = 35	4 * 1 = 4	48 ÷ 8 = 6	45 ÷ 9 = 5
6 × 9 = 54	7 × 5 = 35	35 / 7 = 5	8 / 1 = 8
4 • 7 = 28	6 • 3 = 18	60 ÷ 6 = 10	30 ÷ 3 = 10
1 * 8 = 8	8 * 7 = 56	81 / 9 = 9	16 / 4 = 4
9 × 8 = 72	5 × 8 = 40	20 / 10 = 2	8 / 2 = 4
2 • 10 = 20	9 • 9 = 81	16 ÷ 2 = 8	80 ÷ 10 = 8
0 * 7 = 0	9 * 10 = 90	30 / 5 = 6	36 / 4 = 9
4 × 1 = 4	0 × 0 = 0	49 ÷ 7 = 7	25 ÷ 5 = 5
2 • 4 = 8	1 • 0 = 0	60 / 6 = 10	42 / 7 = 6
10 * 3 = 30	1 * 6 = 6	30 ÷ 3 = 10	36 ÷ 6 = 6
8 × 4 = 32	7 × 2 = 14	8 / 1 = 8	90 / 9 = 10
5 • 8 = 40	6 • 3 = 18	16 ÷ 4 = 4	24 ÷ 8 = 3
4 * 6 = 24	4 * 5 = 20	16 ÷ 8 = 2	6 ÷ 2 = 3
7 × 6 = 42	6 × 6 = 36	40 / 10 = 4	9 / 3 = 3
1 • 8 = 8	10 • 7 = 70	36 ÷ 9 = 4	1 ÷ 1 = 1

Name ______________________

PATH to FLUENCY

Play Quotient Match and Division Blockout

Read the rules for playing a game.
Then play the game.

Rules for Quotient Match

Number of players: 2 or 3

What each player will need: Division Strategy Cards for 6s, 7s, and 8s

1. Shuffle the cards. Put the division cards, sides without answers, face up on the table in 6 rows of 4.
2. Players take turns. On each turn, a player chooses three cards that he or she thinks have the same quotient and turns them over.
3. If all three cards do have the same quotient the player takes them. If the cards do not have the same quotient, the player turns them back over so the without answers side is up.
4. Play continues until no cards remain.

Rules for Division Blockout

Number of players: 3

What each player will need: *Blockout* Game Board (TRB M70), Division Strategy Cards for 6s, 7s, and 8s

1. Players do not write anything on the game board. The first row is for 6s, the second row for 7s, and the third row for 8s, as indicated in the gray column on the left.
2. Each player shuffles his or her Division Strategy Cards for 6s, 7s, 8s, making sure the division sides without answers are face up.
3. Repeat Steps 2, 3, and 4 above. This time players will place the Strategy Cards in the appropriate row to indicate whether the unknown factor is 6, 7, or 8.

PATH to FLUENCY Play Multiplication Blockout

Read the rules for playing *Multiplication Blockout*. Then play the game.

Rules for *Multiplication Block Out*

Number of players: 3

What each player will need: *Blockout* Game Board (TRB M70), Multiplication Strategy Cards for 6s, 7s, and 8s

1. Players choose any 5 factors from 2–9 and write them in any order in the gray spaces at the top of the game board. The players then write the products in the large white spaces. The result will be a scrambled multiplication table.

2. Once the table is complete, players cut off the gray row and gray column that show the factors so that only the products are showing. This will be the game board.

3. Each player shuffles his or her Multiplication Strategy Cards for 6s, 7s, and 8s, making sure the multiplication sides without answers are facing up.

4. One player says, "Go!" and everyone quickly places their Strategy Cards on the game board spaces showing the corresponding products. When a player's game board is completely filled, he or she calls out, "Blockout!"

5. Everyone stops and checks the player's work. If all the cards are placed correctly, that player is the winner. If the player has made a mistake, he or she sits out and waits for the next player to call out, "Blockout!"

Name ______________________________

PATH to FLUENCY Solve Word Problems with 6s, 7s, 8s

Write an equation and solve the problem.

1. Terri's class has 32 students. The students worked on an art project in groups of 4 students. How many groups were there?

____

2. Kyle saw 9 ladybugs while he was camping. Each one had 6 legs. How many legs did the 9 ladybugs have in all?

____

3. Adam walks 3 miles a day. How many miles does he walk in a week?

____

4. Nancy's dog Rover eats 6 cups of food a day. In 8 days, how many cups of food does Rover eat?

____

5. The school library has 72 books on the topic of weather. If Tanya arranged the books in 8 equal-sized stacks, how many books were in each stack?

____

6. The 42 trumpet players in the marching band lined up in 6 equal rows. How many trumpet players were in each row?

____

Solve Word Problems with 6s, 7s, and 8s (continued)

Write an equation and solve the problem.

7. Susan is having a party. She has 18 cups. She puts them in 6 equal stacks. How many cups are in each stack?

____

8. Regina made an array with 7 rows of 9 blocks. How many blocks are in the array?

____

9. Mr. Rodriguez plans to invite 40 students to a picnic. The invitations come in packs of 8. How many packs of invitations does Mr. Rodriguez need to buy?

____

10. A classroom has 7 rows of 4 desks. How many desks are there in the classroom?

____

11. Write a word problem for $48 \div 6$ where 6 is the size of the group.

____

____

12. Write a word problem for 7×9 where 9 is the number of items in one group.

____

____

✓ Check Understanding

Explain how you know when a word problem can be solved by using division.

Name ____________________

PATH to FLUENCY Complete a Multiplication Table

1 Look at the factors to complete the Multiplication Table. Leave blanks for the products you do not know.

×	1	2	3	4	5	6	7	8	9	10
1										
2										
3										
4										
5										
6										
7										
8										
9										
10										

2 Write the multiplications you need to practice.

PATH to FLUENCY

Scrambled Multiplication Tables

Complete each table.

A

×										
	6	30	54	60	42	24	18	12	48	36
	2	10	18	20	14	8	6	4	16	12
	10	50	90	100	70	40	30	20	80	60
	8	40	72	80	56	32	24	16	64	48
	5	25	45	50	35	20	15	10	40	30
	1	5	9	10	7	4	3	2	8	6
	9	45	81	90	63	36	27	18	72	54
	4	20	36	40	28	16	12	8	32	24
	7	35	63	70	49	28	21	14	56	42
	3	15	27	30	21	12	9	6	24	18

B

×										
	27	6	24	21	18	15	12	9	3	
	36	8	32	28	24		16	12	4	40
	9	2	8	7	6	5	4	3	1	10
	18	4	16	14		10	8	6	2	20
		14	56	49	42		28	21	7	
	72		64	56	48	40	32	24	8	80
	45	10	40		30	25	20	15	5	
	54	12	48	42	36	30	24	18	6	60
	90		80	70	60		40	30	10	100
	81	18	72		54	45	36	27	9	

C

×										
	100		20		70	50		90		10
	50	15		20	35		30		40	5
	10	3		4	7		6	9		1
		9		12	21	15		27	24	
		6	4	8			12	18	16	2
		12	8	16	28	20		36	32	
	90	27	18	36	63	45	54		72	
		18	12	24		30	36	54	48	6
		21		28	49		42		56	7
		24		32	56	40		72	64	8

D

×										
	48		42	12	36		18	6		30
	56	28		14		70	21		63	35
			70		60			10		50
		20	35		30		15	5	45	
	32			8		40			36	
	8	4		2			3	1		5
		8	14		12		6		18	10
	64		56		48	80	24	8		40
	72	36		18			27		81	
	24		21		18	30		3	27	

Check Understanding

Complete the sentences.

The numbers in the blue boxes are ______________________.

The numbers in the white boxes are ______________________.

Name ____________________

PATH to FLUENCY

Dashes 13–16

Complete each Dash. Check your answers on page 141.

Dash 13 6s and 8s Multiplications	Dash 14 6s and 8s Divisions	Dash 15 7s and 8s Multiplications	Dash 16 7s and 8s Divisions
a. 6 × 9 = ____	a. 72 / 8 = ____	a. 7 × 3 = ____	a. 63 / 7 = ____
b. 8 * 2 = ____	b. 12 ÷ 6 = ____	b. 8 * 5 = ____	b. 80 ÷ 8 = ____
c. 4 • 6 = ____	c. 16 / 8 = ____	c. 2 • 7 = ____	c. 14 / 7 = ____
d. 7 × 8 = ____	d. 24 ÷ 6 = ____	d. 1 × 8 = ____	d. 16 ÷ 8 = ____
e. 6 * 1 = ____	e. 8 / 8 = ____	e. 7 * 9 = ____	e. 7 / 7 = ____
f. 8 • 9 = ____	f. 6 ÷ 6 = ____	f. 8 • 4 = ____	f. 48 ÷ 8 = ____
g. 3 × 6 = ____	g. 40 / 8 = ____	g. 4 × 7 = ____	g. 35 / 7 = ____
h. 4 * 8 = ____	h. 42 ÷ 6 = ____	h. 7 * 8 = ____	h. 32 ÷ 8 = ____
i. 6 • 8 = ____	i. 24 / 8 = ____	i. 7 • 1 = ____	i. 21 / 7 = ____
j. 8 × 1 = ____	j. 18 ÷ 6 = ____	j. 8 × 2 = ____	j. 8 ÷ 8 = ____
k. 2 * 6 = ____	k. 48 / 8 = ____	k. 5 * 7 = ____	k. 28 / 7 = ____
l. 3 • 8 = ____	l. 48 ÷ 6 = ____	l. 9 • 8 = ____	l. 40 ÷ 8 = ____
m. 6 × 5 = ____	m. 64 / 8 = ____	m. 7 × 6 = ____	m. 49 / 7 = ____
n. 8 * 8 = ____	n. 42 ÷ 6 = ____	n. 8 * 3 = ____	n. 72 ÷ 8 = ____
o. 6 • 6 = ____	o. 56 / 8 = ____	o. 7 • 7 = ____	o. 42 / 7 = ____
p. 5 × 8 = ____	p. 30 ÷ 6 = ____	p. 8 × 8 = ____	p. 24 ÷ 8 = ____
q. 6 * 7 = ____	q. 32 / 8 = ____	q. 7 * 0 = ____	q. 56 / 7 = ____
r. 8 × 0 = ____	r. 54 ÷ 6 = ____	r. 6 • 8 = ____	r. 64 ÷ 8 = ____
s. 0 * 6 = ____	s. 80 / 8 = ____	s. 8 × 0 = ____	s. 70 / 7 = ____
t. 6 • 10 = ____	t. 60 ÷ 6 = ____	t. 7 * 10 = ____	t. 56 ÷ 8 = ____

PATH to FLUENCY

Dashes 17–20

Complete each Dash. Check your answers on page 141.

Dash 17 6s and 7s Multiplications	Dash 18 6s and 7s Divisions	Dash 19 6s, 7s, 8s Multiplications	Dash 20 6s, 7s, 8s Divisions
a. 6 × 6 = ___	a. 70 / 7 = ___	a. 7 × 7 = ___	a. 21 / 7 = ___
b. 7 * 7 = ___	b. 60 ÷ 6 = ___	b. 6 • 3 = ___	b. 16 ÷ 8 = ___
c. 3 • 6 = ___	c. 28 / 7 = ___	c. 8 * 6 = ___	c. 54 / 6 = ___
d. 8 × 7 = ___	d. 30 ÷ 6 = ___	d. 6 × 6 = ___	d. 48 ÷ 8 = ___
e. 6 * 1 = ___	e. 42 / 7 = ___	e. 7 • 6 = ___	e. 64 / 8 = ___
f. 7 • 2 = ___	f. 24 ÷ 6 = ___	f. 4 * 7 = ___	f. 42 ÷ 6 = ___
g. 9 × 6 = ___	g. 35 / 7 = ___	g. 9 × 7 = ___	g. 56 / 7 = ___
h. 9 * 7 = ___	h. 12 ÷ 6 = ___	h. 6 • 9 = ___	h. 72 ÷ 8 = ___
i. 6 • 8 = ___	i. 7 / 7 = ___	i. 6 * 4 = ___	i. 18 / 6 = ___
j. 7 × 3 = ___	j. 36 ÷ 6 = ___	j. 8 × 8 = ___	j. 28 / 7 = ___
k. 7 * 6 = ___	k. 21 / 7 = ___	k. 7 • 3 = ___	k. 56 ÷ 8 = ___
l. 1 • 7 = ___	l. 48 ÷ 6 = ___	l. 8 * 7 = ___	l. 30 / 6 = ___
m. 6 × 2 = ___	m. 63 / 7 = ___	m. 6 × 7 = ___	m. 63 ÷ 7 = ___
n. 7 * 5 = ___	n. 6 ÷ 6 = ___	n. 3 • 6 = ___	n. 32 / 8 = ___
o. 4 • 6 = ___	o. 56 / 7 = ___	o. 2 * 7 = ___	o. 48 ÷ 6 = ___
p. 6 × 7 = ___	p. 18 ÷ 6 = ___	p. 9 × 8 = ___	p. 49 / 7 = ___
q. 6 * 5 = ___	q. 49 / 7 = ___	q. 5 • 6 = ___	q. 36 ÷ 6 = ___
r. 7 • 4 = ___	r. 42 ÷ 6 = ___	r. 7 * 8 = ___	r. 24 ÷ 8 = ___
s. 6 × 10 = ___	s. 14 / 7 = ___	s. 3 × 7 = ___	s. 42 / 7 = ___
t. 7 × 10 = ___	t. 54 ÷ 6 = ___	t. 9 • 6 = ___	t. 24 ÷ 6 = ___

Name ____________

PATH to FLUENCY

Dashes 9B–12B

Complete each multiplication and division Dash. Check your answers on page 142.

Dash 9B 2s, 5s, 9s, 10s Multiplications	Dash 10B 2s, 5s, 9s, 10s Divisions	Dash 11B 0s, 1s, 3s, 4s Multiplications	Dash 12B 1s, 3s, 4s Divisions
a. 6 × 2 = ___	a. 18 / 2 = ___	a. 7 × 1 = ___	a. 2 / 1 = ___
b. 9 • 4 = ___	b. 25 ÷ 5 = ___	b. 0 • 6 = ___	b. 28 ÷ 4 = ___
c. 8 * 5 = ___	c. 70 / 10 = ___	c. 4 * 4 = ___	c. 3 / 3 = ___
d. 1 × 10 = ___	d. 54 ÷ 9 = ___	d. 7 × 3 = ___	d. 1 ÷ 1 = ___
e. 2 • 7 = ___	e. 50 / 5 = ___	e. 3 • 1 = ___	e. 40 / 4 = ___
f. 9 * 9 = ___	f. 81 ÷ 9 = ___	f. 4 * 7 = ___	f. 21 ÷ 3 = ___
g. 5 × 6 = ___	g. 8 / 2 = ___	g. 9 × 0 = ___	g. 5 / 1 = ___
h. 10 • 4 = ___	h. 90 ÷ 10 = ___	h. 1 • 1 = ___	h. 16 ÷ 4 = ___
i. 7 * 5 = ___	i. 35 / 5 = ___	i. 3 * 4 = ___	i. 15 / 3 = ___
j. 8 × 2 = ___	j. 27 / 9 = ___	j. 4 × 9 = ___	j. 6 / 1 = ___
k. 10 • 10 = ___	k. 2 ÷ 2 = ___	k. 8 • 1 = ___	k. 12 ÷ 4 = ___
l. 5 * 3 = ___	l. 36 / 9 = ___	l. 3 * 3 = ___	l. 27 / 3 = ___
m. 9 × 7 = ___	m. 45 ÷ 5 = ___	m. 0 × 4 = ___	m. 9 ÷ 1 = ___
n. 9 • 2 = ___	n. 14 / 2 = ___	n. 10 • 3 = ___	n. 8 / 4 = ___
o. 5 * 5 = ___	o. 20 ÷ 10 = ___	o. 6 * 4 = ___	o. 12 ÷ 3 = ___
p. 6 × 9 = ___	p. 9 / 9 = ___	p. 1 × 4 = ___	p. 3 / 1 = ___
q. 5 • 2 = ___	q. 20 ÷ 5 = ___	q. 3 • 6 = ___	q. 36 ÷ 4 = ___
r. 9 * 5 = ___	r. 45 ÷ 9 = ___	r. 4 * 8 = ___	r. 6 ÷ 3 = ___
s. 8 × 10 = ___	s. 5 / 5 = ___	s. 7 × 0 = ___	s. 4 / 1 = ___
t. 5 • 10 = ___	t. 4 ÷ 2 = ___	t. 5 • 3 = ___	t. 4 ÷ 4 = ___

PATH to FLUENCY

Dashes 9C–12C

Complete each Dash. Check your answers on page 142.

Dash 9C 2s, 5 ,9s, 10s Multiplications	Dash 10C 2s, 5, 9s, 10s Divisions	Dash 11C 0s, 1s ,3s, 4s Multiplications	Dash 12C 1s, 3s, 4s Divisions
a. 5 × 8 = ____	a. 36 ÷ 9 = ____	a. 0 × 7 = ____	a. 4 / 1 = ____
b. 9 * 9 = ____	b. 30 / 5 = ____	b. 1 * 4 = ____	b. 15 ÷ 3 = ____
c. 10 • 7 = ____	c. 18 ÷ 2 = ____	c. 3 • 6 = ____	c. 24 / 4 = ____
d. 4 × 5 = ____	d. 80 / 10 = ____	d. 4 × 9 = ____	d. 9 ÷ 1 = ____
e. 5 * 5 = ____	e. 40 ÷ 5 = ____	e. 8 * 0 = ____	e. 21 / 3 = ____
f. 10 • 3 = ____	f. 72 / 9 = ____	f. 7 * 1 = ____	f. 12 ÷ 4 = ____
g. 1 × 5 = ____	g. 6 ÷ 2 = ____	g. 4 • 3 = ____	g. 5 / 1 = ____
h. 3 * 9 = ____	h. 54 / 9 = ____	h. 4 × 4 = ____	h. 3 ÷ 3 = ____
i. 9 • 6 = ____	i. 25 ÷ 5 = ____	i. 0 * 5 = ____	i. 32 / 4 = ____
j. 10 × 8 = ____	j. 10 / 10 = ____	j. 1 • 6 = ____	j. 2 ÷ 1 = ____
k. 2 * 9 = ____	k. 45 ÷ 5 = ____	k. 3 × 2 = ____	k. 18 / 3 = ____
l. 6 • 2 = ____	l. 27 / 9 = ____	l. 4 * 7 = ____	l. 36 ÷ 4 = ____
m. 6 × 10 = ____	m. 14 ÷ 2 = ____	m. 1 • 0 = ____	m. 7 / 1 = ____
n. 8 * 9 = ____	n. 35 / 5 = ____	n. 2 × 1 = ____	n. 24 ÷ 3 = ____
o. 8 • 2 = ____	o. 90 ÷ 9 = ____	o. 9 * 3 = ____	o. 4 / 4 = ____
p. 4 × 2 = ____	p. 90 / 10 = ____	p. 2 • 4 = ____	p. 6 ÷ 1 = ____
q. 10 * 5 = ____	q. 63 ÷ 9 = ____	q. 0 × 3 = ____	q. 12 / 3 = ____
r. 10 • 10 = ____	r. 15 / 5 = ____	r. 1 * 1 = ____	r. 20 ÷ 4 = ____
s. 9 × 6 = ____	s. 50 ÷ 10 = ____	s. 3 • 9 = ____	s. 8 / 1 = ____
t. 5 * 7 = ____	t. 8 / 2 = ____	t. 4 × 5 = ____	t. 27 ÷ 3 = ____

Name

PATH to FLUENCY

Answers to Dashes 13–20

Use this sheet to check your answers to the Dashes on pages 137 and 138.

Dash 13 ×	Dash 14 ÷	Dash 15 ×	Dash 16 ÷	Dash 17 ×	Dash 18 ÷	Dash 19 ×	Dash 20 ÷
a. 54	a. 9	a. 21	a. 9	a. 36	a. 10	a. 49	a. 3
b. 16	b. 2	b. 40	b. 10	b. 49	b. 10	b. 18	b. 2
c. 24	c. 2	c. 14	c. 2	c. 18	c. 4	c. 48	c. 9
d. 56	d. 4	d. 8	d. 2	d. 56	d. 5	d. 36	d. 6
e. 6	e. 1	e. 63	e. 1	e. 6	e. 6	e. 42	e. 8
f. 72	f. 1	f. 32	f. 6	f. 14	f. 4	f. 28	f. 7
g. 18	g. 5	g. 28	g. 5	g. 54	g. 5	g. 63	g. 8
h. 32	h. 7	h. 56	h. 4	h. 63	h. 2	h. 54	h. 9
i. 48	i. 3	i. 7	i. 3	i. 48	i. 1	i. 24	i. 3
j. 8	j. 3	j. 16	j. 1	j. 21	j. 6	j. 64	j. 4
k. 12	k. 6	k. 35	k. 4	k. 42	k. 3	k. 21	k. 7
l. 24	l. 8	l. 72	l. 5	l. 7	l. 8	l. 56	l. 5
m. 30	m. 8	m. 42	m. 7	m. 12	m. 9	m. 42	m. 9
n. 64	n. 7	n. 24	n. 9	n. 35	n. 1	n. 18	n. 4
o. 36	o. 7	o. 49	o. 6	o. 24	o. 8	o. 14	o. 8
p. 40	p. 5	p. 64	p. 3	p. 42	p. 3	p. 72	p. 7
q. 42	q. 4	q. 0	q. 8	q. 30	q. 7	q. 30	q. 6
r. 0	r. 9	r. 48	r. 8	r. 28	r. 7	r. 56	r. 3
s. 0	s. 10	s. 0	s. 10	s. 60	s. 2	s. 21	s. 6
t. 60	t. 10	t. 70	t. 7	t. 70	t. 9	t. 54	t. 4

PATH to FLUENCY Answers to Dashes 9B–12B, 9C–12C

Use this sheet to check your answers to the Dashes on pages 139 and 140.

Dash 9B ×	Dash 10B ÷	Dash 11B ×	Dash 12B ÷	Dash 9C ×	Dash 10C ÷	Dash 11C ×	Dash 12C ÷
a. 12	a. 9	a. 7	a. 2	a. 40	a. 4	a. 0	a. 4
b. 36	b. 5	b. 0	b. 7	b. 81	b. 6	b. 4	b. 5
c. 40	c. 7	c. 16	c. 1	c. 70	c. 9	c. 18	c. 6
d. 10	d. 6	d. 21	d. 1	d. 20	d. 8	d. 36	d. 9
e. 14	e. 10	e. 3	e. 10	e. 25	e. 8	e. 0	e. 7
f. 81	f. 9	f. 28	f. 7	f. 30	f. 8	f. 7	f. 3
g. 30	g. 4	g. 0	g. 5	g. 5	g. 3	g. 12	g. 5
h. 40	h. 9	h. 1	h. 4	h. 27	h. 6	h. 16	h. 1
i. 35	i. 7	i. 12	i. 5	i. 54	i. 5	i. 0	i. 8
j. 16	j. 3	j. 36	j. 6	j. 80	j. 1	j. 6	j. 2
k. 100	k. 1	k. 8	k. 3	k. 18	k. 9	k. 6	k. 6
l. 15	l. 4	l. 9	l. 9	l. 12	l. 3	l. 28	l. 9
m. 63	m. 9	m. 0	m. 9	m. 60	m. 7	m. 0	m. 7
n. 18	n. 7	n. 30	n. 2	n. 72	n. 7	n. 2	n. 8
o. 25	o. 2	o. 24	o. 4	o. 16	o. 10	o. 27	o. 1
p. 54	p. 1	p. 4	p. 3	p. 8	p. 9	p. 8	p. 6
q. 10	q. 4	q. 18	q. 9	q. 50	q. 7	q. 0	q. 4
r. 45	r. 5	r. 32	r. 2	r. 100	r. 3	r. 1	r. 5
s. 80	s. 1	s. 0	s. 4	s. 54	s. 5	s. 27	s. 8
t. 50	t. 2	t. 15	t. 1	t. 35	t. 4	t. 20	t. 9

Name ______________________________

PATH to FLUENCY

Dashes 21–22, 19A–20A

Complete each Dash. Check your answers on page 161.

Dash 21 **2s, 3s, 4s, 5s, 9s** **Multiplications**	**Dash 22** **2s, 3s, 4s, 5s, 9s** **Divisions**	**Dash 19A** **6s, 7s, 8s** **Multiplications**	**Dash 20A** **6s, 7s, 8s** **Divisions**
a. 6 × 3 = ___	a. 16 / 4 = ___	a. 9 × 6 = ___	a. 24 ÷ 6 = ___
b. 4 • 7 = ___	b. 54 ÷ 9 = ___	b. 7 * 7 = ___	b. 21 / 7 = ___
c. 8 * 2 = ___	c. 4 / 2 = ___	c. 3 • 7 = ___	c. 42 ÷ 7 = ___
d. 5 × 3 = ___	d. 28 ÷ 4 = ___	d. 6 × 3 = ___	d. 16 / 8 = ___
e. 4 • 4 = ___	e. 25 / 5 = ___	e. 7 * 8 = ___	e. 24 ÷ 8 = ___
f. 3 • 9 = ___	f. 21 ÷ 3 = ___	f. 8 • 6 = ___	f. 54 / 6 = ___
g. 9 × 9 = ___	g. 40 / 4 = ___	g. 5 × 6 = ___	g. 36 ÷ 6 = ___
h. 8 • 9 = ___	h. 81 ÷ 9 = ___	h. 6 * 6 = ___	h. 48 / 8 = ___
i. 6 * 4 = ___	i. 35 / 5 = ___	i. 9 • 8 = ___	i. 49 ÷ 7 = ___
j. 3 × 3 = ___	j. 12 / 3 = ___	j. 7 × 6 = ___	j. 64 / 8 = ___
k. 2 • 7 = ___	k. 2 ÷ 2 = ___	k. 2 * 7 = ___	k. 48 ÷ 6 = ___
l. 8 • 5 = ___	l. 63 / 9 = ___	l. 4 • 7 = ___	l. 42 / 6 = ___
m. 4 × 9 = ___	m. 36 ÷ 4 = ___	m. 3 × 6 = ___	m. 32 ÷ 8 = ___
n. 9 • 5 = ___	n. 18 / 2 = ___	n. 9 * 7 = ___	n. 56 / 7 = ___
o. 7 * 3 = ___	o. 9 ÷ 3 = ___	o. 6 • 7 = ___	o. 63 ÷ 7 = ___
p. 2 × 2 = ___	p. 36 / 9 = ___	p. 6 × 9 = ___	p. 72 / 8 = ___
q. 8 • 4 = ___	q. 40 ÷ 5 = ___	q. 8 * 7 = ___	q. 30 ÷ 6 = ___
r. 5 * 1 = ___	r. 12 ÷ 4 = ___	r. 6 • 4 = ___	r. 18 / 6 = ___
s. 5 × 5 = ___	s. 9 / 9 = ___	s. 7 × 3 = ___	s. 56 ÷ 8 = ___
t. 6 • 9 = ___	t. 14 ÷ 2 = ___	t. 8 * 8 = ___	t. 28 / 7 = ___

PATH to FLUENCY

Dashes 21A–22A, 19B–20B

Complete each Dash. Check your answers on page 161.

Dash 21A 2s, 3s, 4s, 5s, 9s Multiplications	Dash 22A 2s, 3s, 4s, 5s, 9s Divisions	Dash 19B 6s, 7s, 8s Multiplications	Dash 20B 6s, 7s, 8s Divisions
a. 6 × 9 = ___	a. 14 ÷ 2 = ___	a. 6 × 2 = ___	a. 36 ÷ 6 = ___
b. 6 * 3 = ___	b. 16 / 4 = ___	b. 7 * 7 = ___	b. 63 / 7 = ___
c. 4 • 7 = ___	c. 9 ÷ 9 = ___	c. 8 • 5 = ___	c. 24 ÷ 8 = ___
d. 5 × 5 = ___	d. 54 / 9 = ___	d. 4 × 6 = ___	d. 18 / 6 = ___
e. 8 * 2 = ___	e. 12 ÷ 4 = ___	e. 3 * 7 = ___	e. 28 ÷ 7 = ___
f. 5 • 1 = ___	f. 4 / 2 = ___	f. 1 • 8 = ___	f. 48 / 8 = ___
g. 5 × 3 = ___	g. 40 ÷ 5 = ___	g. 6 × 9 = ___	g. 54 ÷ 6 = ___
h. 8 * 4 = ___	h. 28 / 4 = ___	h. 7 * 5 = ___	h. 42 / 7 = ___
i. 4 • 4 = ___	i. 36 ÷ 9 = ___	i. 8 • 3 = ___	i. 72 ÷ 8 = ___
j. 2 × 2 = ___	j. 25 / 5 = ___	j. 4 × 6 = ___	j. 6 / 6 = ___
k. 3 * 9 = ___	k. 9 ÷ 3 = ___	k. 9 * 7 = ___	k. 14 ÷ 7 = ___
l. 7 • 3 = ___	l. 21 / 3 = ___	l. 8 • 8 = ___	l. 56 / 8 = ___
m. 9 × 9 = ___	m. 18 ÷ 2 = ___	m. 6 × 1 = ___	m. 12 ÷ 6 = ___
n. 9 * 5 = ___	n. 40 / 4 = ___	n. 7 * 4 = ___	n. 7 / 7 = ___
o. 8 • 9 = ___	o. 36 ÷ 4 = ___	o. 8 • 6 = ___	o. 16 ÷ 8 = ___
p. 4 × 9 = ___	p. 81 / 9 = ___	p. 7 × 6 = ___	p. 30 / 6 = ___
q. 6 * 4 = ___	q. 63 ÷ 9 = ___	q. 2 * 7 = ___	q. 56 ÷ 7 = ___
r. 8 • 5 = ___	r. 35 / 5 = ___	r. 9 • 8 = ___	r. 8 / 8 = ___
s. 2 × 7 = ___	s. 12 ÷ 3 = ___	s. 6 × 5 = ___	s. 48 ÷ 6 = ___
t. 3 * 3 = ___	t. 2 / 2 = ___	t. 7 * 6 = ___	t. 21 / 7 = ___

Name ____________

PATH to FLUENCY

Dashes 21B–22B, 19C–20C

Complete each Dash. Check your answers on page 162.

Dash 21B 2s, 3s, 4s, 5s, 9s Multiplications	Dash 22B 2s, 3s, 4s, 5s, 9s Divisions	Dash 19C 6s, 7s, 8s Multiplications	Dash 20C 6s, 7s, 8s Divisions
a. 2 × 3 = ___	a. 8 ÷ 2 = ___	a. 6 × 8 = ___	a. 54 ÷ 6 = ___
b. 3 * 8 = ___	b. 18 / 3 = ___	b. 7 * 3 = ___	b. 49 / 7 = ___
c. 4 • 4 = ___	c. 12 ÷ 4 = ___	c. 8 • 6 = ___	c. 24 ÷ 8 = ___
d. 5 × 6 = ___	d. 25 / 5 = ___	d. 2 × 6 = ___	d. 6 / 6 = ___
e. 9 * 8 = ___	e. 63 ÷ 9 = ___	e. 8 * 7 = ___	e. 35 ÷ 7 = ___
f. 9 • 2 = ___	f. 16 / 2 = ___	f. 9 • 8 = ___	f. 72 / 8 = ___
g. 3 × 3 = ___	g. 3 ÷ 3 = ___	g. 6 × 4 = ___	g. 18 ÷ 6 = ___
h. 4 * 2 = ___	h. 28 / 4 = ___	h. 7 * 1 = ___	h. 28 / 7 = ___
i. 9 • 5 = ___	i. 45 ÷ 5 = ___	i. 8 • 3 = ___	i. 8 ÷ 8 = ___
j. 9 × 4 = ___	j. 27 / 9 = ___	j. 5 × 6 = ___	j. 30 / 6 = ___
k. 2 * 7 = ___	k. 12 ÷ 2 = ___	k. 9 * 7 = ___	k. 21 ÷ 7 = ___
l. 3 • 5 = ___	l. 12 / 3 = ___	l. 4 • 8 = ___	l. 40 / 8 = ___
m. 4 × 8 = ___	m. 20 ÷ 4 = ___	m. 6 × 6 = ___	m. 42 ÷ 6 = ___
n. 5 * 3 = ___	n. 40 / 5 = ___	n. 7 * 5 = ___	n. 63 / 7 = ___
o. 9 • 6 = ___	o. 54 ÷ 9 = ___	o. 8 • 8 = ___	o. 32 ÷ 8 = ___
p. 2 × 8 = ___	p. 2 / 2 = ___	p. 1 × 6 = ___	p. 36 / 6 = ___
q. 3 * 7 = ___	q. 9 ÷ 3 = ___	q. 2 * 7 = ___	q. 14 ÷ 7 = ___
r. 4 • 1 = ___	r. 36 / 4 = ___	r. 5 • 8 = ___	r. 56 / 8 = ___
s. 5 × 8 = ___	s. 15 ÷ 5 = ___	s. 6 × 9 = ___	s. 24 ÷ 6 = ___
t. 9 * 9 = ___	t. 9 / 9 = ___	t. 7 * 7 = ___	t. 42 / 7 = ___

PATH to FLUENCY Dashes 21C–22C, 19D–20D

Complete each Dash. Check your answers on page 162.

Dash 21C 2s, 3s, 4s, 5s, 9s Multiplications	Dash 22C 2s, 3s, 4s, 5s, 9s Divisions	Dash 19D 6s, 7s, 8s Multiplications	Dash 20D 6s, 7s, 8s Divisions
a. 2 × 9 = ___	a. 8 ÷ 2 = ___	a. 6 × 9 = ___	a. 18 / 6 = ___
b. 3 * 7 = ___	b. 6 / 3 = ___	b. 7 * 6 = ___	b. 42 ÷ 7 = ___
c. 4 • 5 = ___	c. 4 ÷ 4 = ___	c. 8 • 2 = ___	c. 32 / 8 = ___
d. 5 × 3 = ___	d. 20 / 5 = ___	d. 3 × 6 = ___	d. 54 ÷ 6 = ___
e. 9 * 1 = ___	e. 63 ÷ 9 = ___	e. 4 * 7 = ___	e. 49 / 7 = ___
f. 1 • 2 = ___	f. 16 / 2 = ___	f. 9 • 8 = ___	f. 8 / 8 = ___
g. 4 × 3 = ___	g. 15 ÷ 3 = ___	g. 6 × 6 = ___	g. 30 ÷ 6 = ___
h. 4 * 1 = ___	h. 32 / 4 = ___	h. 7 * 2 = ___	h. 35 / 7 = ___
i. 7 • 5 = ___	i. 30 ÷ 5 = ___	i. 8 • 1 = ___	i. 48 ÷ 8 = ___
j. 9 × 9 = ___	j. 45 / 9 = ___	j. 2 × 6 = ___	j. 24 / 6 = ___
k. 2 * 3 = ___	k. 2 ÷ 2 = ___	k. 8 * 7 = ___	k. 14 ÷ 7 = ___
l. 3 • 8 = ___	l. 21 / 3 = ___	l. 3 • 8 = ___	l. 56 / 8 = ___
m. 4 × 4 = ___	m. 12 ÷ 4 = ___	m. 6 × 4 = ___	m. 6 ÷ 6 = ___
n. 5 * 2 = ___	n. 10 / 5 = ___	n. 7 * 5 = ___	n. 21 / 7 = ___
o. 9 • 6 = ___	o. 9 ÷ 9 = ___	o. 8 • 8 = ___	o. 40 ÷ 8 = ___
p. 6 × 2 = ___	p. 12 / 2 = ___	p. 1 × 6 = ___	p. 48 / 6 = ___
q. 9 * 3 = ___	q. 27 ÷ 3 = ___	q. 3 * 7 = ___	q. 56 ÷ 7 = ___
r. 6 • 4 = ___	r. 20 / 4 = ___	r. 4 • 8 = ___	r. 64 / 8 = ___
s. 5 × 5 = ___	s. 40 ÷ 8 = ___	s. 6 × 7 = ___	s. 36 ÷ 6 = ___
t. 3 * 9 = ___	t. 81 / 9 = ___	t. 7 * 7 = ___	t. 7 / 7 = ___

Name

Answers to Dashes 21–22, 19A–22A, 19B–20B

Use this sheet to check your answers to the Dashes on pages 157 and 158.

Dash 21 ×	Dash 22 ÷	Dash 19A ×	Dash 20A ÷	Dash 21A ×	Dash 22A ÷	Dash 19B ×	Dash 20B ÷
a. 18	a. 4	a. 54	a. 4	a. 54	a. 7	a. 12	a. 6
b. 28	b. 6	b. 49	b. 3	b. 18	b. 4	b. 49	b. 9
c. 16	c. 2	c. 21	c. 6	c. 28	c. 1	c. 40	c. 3
d. 15	d. 7	d. 18	d. 2	d. 25	d. 6	d. 24	d. 3
e. 16	e. 5	e. 56	e. 3	e. 16	e. 3	e. 21	e. 4
f. 27	f. 7	f. 48	f. 9	f. 5	f. 2	f. 8	f. 6
g. 81	g. 10	g. 30	g. 6	g. 15	g. 8	g. 54	g. 9
h. 72	h. 9	h. 36	h. 6	h. 32	h. 7	h. 35	h. 6
i. 24	i. 7	i. 72	i. 7	i. 16	i. 4	i. 24	i. 9
j. 9	j. 4	j. 42	j. 8	j. 4	j. 5	j. 24	j. 1
k. 14	k. 1	k. 14	k. 8	k. 27	k. 3	k. 63	k. 2
l. 40	l. 7	l. 28	l. 7	l. 21	l. 7	l. 64	l. 7
m. 36	m. 9	m. 18	m. 4	m. 81	m. 9	m. 6	m. 2
n. 45	n. 9	n. 63	n. 8	n. 45	n. 10	n. 28	n. 1
o. 21	o. 3	o. 42	o. 9	o. 72	o. 9	o. 48	o. 2
p. 4	p. 4	p. 54	p. 9	p. 36	p. 9	p. 42	p. 5
q. 32	q. 8	q. 56	q. 5	q. 24	q. 7	q. 14	q. 8
r. 5	r. 3	r. 24	r. 3	r. 40	r. 7	r. 72	r. 1
s. 25	s. 1	s. 21	s. 7	s. 14	s. 4	s. 30	s. 8
t. 54	t. 7	t. 64	t. 4	t. 9	t. 1	t. 42	t. 3

Answers to Dashes 21B–22B, 19C–22C, 19D–20D

Use this sheet to check your answers to the Dashes on pages 159 and 160.

	Dash 21B ×	Dash 22B ÷	Dash 19C ×	Dash 20C ÷	Dash 21C ×	Dash 22C ÷	Dash 19D ×	Dash 20D ÷
a.	6	4	48	9	18	4	54	3
b.	24	6	21	7	21	2	42	6
c.	16	3	48	3	20	1	16	4
d.	30	5	12	1	15	4	18	9
e.	72	7	56	5	9	7	28	7
f.	18	8	72	9	2	8	72	1
g.	9	1	24	3	12	5	36	5
h.	8	7	7	4	4	8	14	5
i.	45	9	24	1	35	6	8	6
j.	36	3	30	5	81	5	12	4
k.	14	6	63	3	6	1	56	2
l.	15	4	32	5	24	7	24	7
m.	32	5	36	7	16	3	24	1
n.	15	8	35	9	10	2	35	3
o.	54	6	64	4	54	1	64	5
p.	16	1	6	6	12	6	6	8
q.	21	3	14	2	27	9	21	8
r.	4	9	40	7	24	5	32	8
s.	40	3	54	4	25	5	42	6
t.	81	1	49	6	27	9	49	1

Name ____________________

PATH to FLUENCY

Play *Division Three-in-a-Row*

Rules for *Division Three-in-a-Row*

Number of players: 2

What You Will Need: Product Cards, one *Three-in-a-Row* Game Grid for each player

1. Players write a number in each of the squares on their game grids. They may use only numbers from 1 to 9, but they may use the same number more than once.

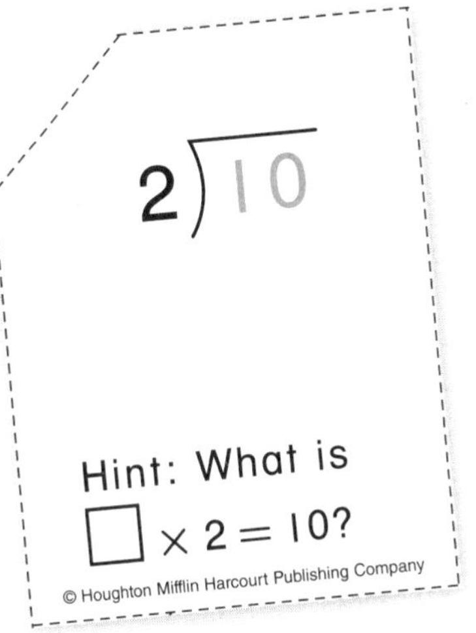

2. Shuffle the cards. Place them division side up in a stack in the center of the table.

3. Players take turns. On each turn, a player completes the division on the top card and then partners check the answer.

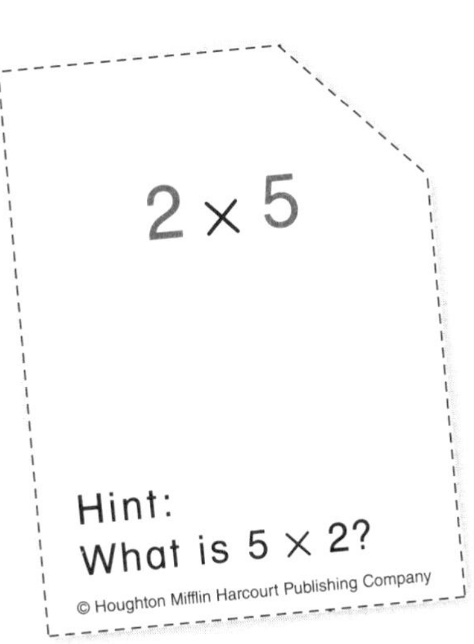

4. For a correct answer, if the quotient is on the game grid, the player puts an X through that grid square. If the answer is wrong, or if the quotient is not on the grid, the player doesn't mark anything. The player puts the card division side up on the bottom of the stack.

5. The first player to mark three squares in a row (horizontally, vertically, or diagonally) wins.

2×2

$2 \bullet 3$

Hint:
What is $3 \cdot 2$?

$2 * 4$

Hint:
What is $4 * 2$?

2×5

Hint:
What is 5×2?

2×6

Hint:
What is 6×2?

$2 \bullet 7$

Hint:
What is $7 \cdot 2$?

$2 * 8$

Hint:
What is $8 * 2$?

2×9

Hint:
What is 9×2?

5×2

Hint:
What is 2×5?

$5 \bullet 3$

Hint:
What is $3 \cdot 5$?

$5 * 4$

Hint:
What is $4 * 5$?

5×5

5×6

Hint:
What is 6×5?

$5 \bullet 7$

Hint:
What is $7 \cdot 5$?

$5 * 8$

Hint:
What is $8 * 5$?

5×9

Hint:
What is 9×5?

$2\overline{)10}$

Hint: What is

☐ × 2 = 10?

$2\overline{)8}$

Hint: What is

☐ × 2 = 8?

$2\overline{)6}$

Hint: What is

☐ × 2 = 6?

$2\overline{)4}$

Hint: What is

☐ × 2 = 4?

$2\overline{)18}$

Hint: What is

☐ × 2 = 18?

$2\overline{)16}$

Hint: What is

☐ × 2 = 16?

$2\overline{)14}$

Hint: What is

☐ × 2 = 14?

$2\overline{)12}$

Hint: What is

☐ × 2 = 12?

$5\overline{)25}$

Hint: What is

☐ × 5 = 25?

$5\overline{)20}$

Hint: What is

☐ × 5 = 20?

$5\overline{)15}$

Hint: What is

☐ × 5 = 15?

$5\overline{)10}$

Hint: What is

☐ × 5 = 10?

$5\overline{)45}$

Hint: What is

☐ × 5 = 45?

$5\overline{)40}$

Hint: What is

☐ × 5 = 40?

$5\overline{)35}$

Hint: What is

☐ × 5 = 35?

$5\overline{)30}$

Hint: What is

☐ × 5 = 30?

9×2

Hint:
What is 2×9?

$9 \bullet 3$

Hint:
What is $3 \cdot 9$?

$9 * 4$

Hint:
What is $4 * 9$?

9×5

Hint:
What is 5×9?

9×6

Hint:
What is 6×9?

$9 \bullet 7$

Hint:
What is $7 \cdot 9$?

$9 * 8$

Hint:
What is $8 * 9$?

9×9

$\times$ $\bullet$ $*$ $\times$

$\times$ $\bullet$ $*$ $\times$

You can write any numbers on the last 8 cards. Use them to practice difficult problems or if you lose a card.

$9\overline{)45}$

Hint: What is
☐ × 9 = 45?

$9\overline{)36}$

Hint: What is
☐ × 9 = 36?

$9\overline{)27}$

Hint: What is
☐ × 9 = 27?

$9\overline{)18}$

Hint: What is
☐ × 9 = 18?

$9\overline{)81}$

Hint: What is
☐ × 9 = 81?

$9\overline{)72}$

Hint: What is
☐ × 9 = 72?

$9\overline{)63}$

Hint: What is
☐ × 9 = 63?

$9\overline{)54}$

Hint: What is
☐ × 9 = 54?

You can write any numbers on the last 8 cards. Use them to practice difficult problems or if you lose a card.

3×2

Hint:
What is 2×3?

$3 \bullet 3$

$3 * 4$

Hint:
What is $4 * 3$?

3×5

Hint:
What is 5×3?

3×6

Hint:
What is 6×3?

$3 \bullet 7$

Hint:
What is $7 \cdot 3$?

$3 * 8$

Hint:
What is $8 * 3$?

3×9

Hint:
What is 9×3?

4×2

Hint:
What is 2×4?

$4 \bullet 3$

Hint:
What is $3 \cdot 4$?

$4 * 4$

4×5

Hint:
What is 5×4?

4×6

Hint:
What is 6×4?

$4 \bullet 7$

Hint:
What is $7 \cdot 4$?

$4 * 8$

Hint:
What is $8 * 4$?

4×9

Hint:
What is 9×4?

$3\overline{)15}$

Hint: What is □ × 3 = 15?

$3\overline{)12}$

Hint: What is □ × 3 = 12?

$3\overline{)9}$

Hint: What is □ × 3 = 9?

$3\overline{)6}$

Hint: What is □ × 3 = 6?

$3\overline{)27}$

Hint: What is □ × 3 = 27?

$3\overline{)24}$

Hint: What is □ × 3 = 24?

$3\overline{)21}$

Hint: What is □ × 3 = 21?

$3\overline{)18}$

Hint: What is □ × 3 = 18?

$4\overline{)20}$

Hint: What is □ × 4 = 20?

$4\overline{)16}$

Hint: What is □ × 4 = 16?

$4\overline{)12}$

Hint: What is □ × 4 = 12?

$4\overline{)8}$

Hint: What is □ × 4 = 8?

$4\overline{)36}$

Hint: What is □ × 4 = 36?

$4\overline{)32}$

Hint: What is □ × 4 = 32?

$4\overline{)28}$

Hint: What is □ × 4 = 28?

$4\overline{)24}$

Hint: What is □ × 4 = 24?

6×2

Hint:
What is 2×6?

$6 \bullet 3$

Hint:
What is $3 \cdot 6$?

$6 * 4$

Hint:
What is $4 * 6$?

6×5

Hint:
What is 5×6?

6×6

$6 \bullet 7$

Hint:
What is $7 \cdot 6$?

$6 * 8$

Hint:
What is $8 * 6$?

6×9

Hint:
What is 9×6?

7×2

Hint:
What is 2×7?

$7 \bullet 3$

Hint:
What is $3 \cdot 7$?

$7 * 4$

Hint:
What is $4 * 7$?

7×5

Hint:
What is 5×7?

7×6

Hint:
What is 6×7?

$7 \bullet 7$

$7 * 8$

Hint:
What is $8 * 7$?

7×9

Hint:
What is 9×7?

$6\overline{)30}$

Hint: What is
☐ × 6 = 30?

$6\overline{)24}$

Hint: What is
☐ × 6 = 24?

$6\overline{)18}$

Hint: What is
☐ × 6 = 18?

$6\overline{)12}$

Hint: What is
☐ × 6 = 12?

$6\overline{)54}$

Hint: What is
☐ × 6 = 54?

$6\overline{)48}$

Hint: What is
☐ × 6 = 48?

$6\overline{)42}$

Hint: What is
☐ × 6 = 42?

$6\overline{)36}$

Hint: What is
☐ × 6 = 36?

$7\overline{)35}$

Hint: What is
☐ × 7 = 35?

$7\overline{)28}$

Hint: What is
☐ × 7 = 28?

$7\overline{)21}$

Hint: What is
☐ × 7 = 21?

$7\overline{)14}$

Hint: What is
☐ × 7 = 14?

$7\overline{)63}$

Hint: What is
☐ × 7 = 63?

$7\overline{)56}$

Hint: What is
☐ × 7 = 56?

$7\overline{)49}$

Hint: What is
☐ × 7 = 49?

$7\overline{)42}$

Hint: What is
☐ × 7 = 42?

8 × 2

Hint:
What is 2 × 8?

8 • 3

Hint:
What is 3 • 8?

8 * 4

Hint:
What is 4 * 8?

8 × 5

Hint:
What is 5 × 8?

8 × 6

Hint:
What is 6 × 8?

8 • 7

Hint:
What is 7 • 8?

8 * 8

8 × 9

Hint:
What is 9 × 8?

×

•

*

×

×

•

*

×

You can write any numbers on the last 8 cards. Use them to practice difficult problems or if you lose a card.

$8\overline{)40}$

Hint: What is

☐ × 8 = 40?

$8\overline{)32}$

Hint: What is

☐ × 8 = 32?

$8\overline{)24}$

Hint: What is

☐ × 8 = 24?

$8\overline{)16}$

Hint: What is

☐ × 8 = 16?

$8\overline{)72}$

Hint: What is

☐ × 8 = 72?

$8\overline{)64}$

Hint: What is

☐ × 8 = 64?

$8\overline{)56}$

Hint: What is

☐ × 8 = 56?

$8\overline{)48}$

Hint: What is

☐ × 8 = 48?

You can write any numbers on the last 8 cards. Use them to practice difficult problems or if you lose a card.

Name ______________________

PATH to FLUENCY

Diagnostic Checkup for Basic Multiplication

1. $7 \times 5 =$ ___	2. $2 \times 3 =$ ___	3. $9 \times 9 =$ ___	4. $9 \times 6 =$ ___
5. $6 \times 2 =$ ___	6. $3 \times 0 =$ ___	7. $3 \times 4 =$ ___	8. $6 \times 8 =$ ___
9. $5 \times 9 =$ ___	10. $3 \times 3 =$ ___	11. $2 \times 9 =$ ___	12. $5 \times 7 =$ ___
13. $6 \times 10 =$ ___	14. $4 \times 1 =$ ___	15. $6 \times 4 =$ ___	16. $4 \times 8 =$ ___
17. $5 \times 2 =$ ___	18. $1 \times 3 =$ ___	19. $3 \times 9 =$ ___	20. $7 \times 6 =$ ___
21. $7 \times 2 =$ ___	22. $9 \times 0 =$ ___	23. $8 \times 9 =$ ___	24. $8 \times 7 =$ ___
25. $8 \times 10 =$ ___	26. $6 \times 3 =$ ___	27. $4 \times 4 =$ ___	28. $3 \times 8 =$ ___
29. $5 \times 5 =$ ___	30. $6 \times 0 =$ ___	31. $7 \times 9 =$ ___	32. $6 \times 6 =$ ___
33. $9 \times 2 =$ ___	34. $8 \times 3 =$ ___	35. $5 \times 4 =$ ___	36. $7 \times 7 =$ ___
37. $5 \times 10 =$ ___	38. $5 \times 1 =$ ___	39. $10 \times 9 =$ ___	40. $5 \times 6 =$ ___
41. $6 \times 5 =$ ___	42. $9 \times 3 =$ ___	43. $4 \times 2 =$ ___	44. $7 \times 8 =$ ___
45. $8 \times 2 =$ ___	46. $5 \times 0 =$ ___	47. $4 \times 9 =$ ___	48. $6 \times 7 =$ ___
49. $9 \times 5 =$ ___	50. $6 \times 1 =$ ___	51. $7 \times 4 =$ ___	52. $9 \times 8 =$ ___
53. $4 \times 10 =$ ___	54. $5 \times 3 =$ ___	55. $6 \times 9 =$ ___	56. $8 \times 6 =$ ___
57. $8 \times 5 =$ ___	58. $8 \times 0 =$ ___	59. $8 \times 4 =$ ___	60. $4 \times 7 =$ ___
61. $3 \times 5 =$ ___	62. $7 \times 3 =$ ___	63. $5 \times 9 =$ ___	64. $3 \times 6 =$ ___
65. $7 \times 10 =$ ___	66. $8 \times 1 =$ ___	67. $0 \times 4 =$ ___	68. $9 \times 7 =$ ___
69. $4 \times 5 =$ ___	70. $4 \times 3 =$ ___	71. $1 \times 9 =$ ___	72. $8 \times 8 =$ ___

Name ______

PATH to FLUENCY Diagnostic Checkup for Basic Division

1. 12 ÷ 2 = ____
2. 8 ÷ 1 = ____
3. 36 ÷ 9 = ____
4. 35 ÷ 7 = ____
5. 20 ÷ 5 = ____
6. 24 ÷ 3 = ____
7. 12 ÷ 4 = ____
8. 6 ÷ 6 = ____
9. 6 ÷ 2 = ____
10. 3 ÷ 3 = ____
11. 18 ÷ 9 = ____
12. 63 ÷ 7 = ____
13. 20 ÷ 10 = ____
14. 0 ÷ 1 = ____
15. 40 ÷ 4 = ____
16. 48 ÷ 8 = ____
17. 18 ÷ 2 = ____
18. 6 ÷ 3 = ____
19. 8 ÷ 4 = ____
20. 36 ÷ 6 = ____
21. 8 ÷ 2 = ____
22. 9 ÷ 1 = ____
23. 9 ÷ 9 = ____
24. 56 ÷ 7 = ____
25. 40 ÷ 5 = ____
26. 9 ÷ 3 = ____
27. 36 ÷ 4 = ____
28. 56 ÷ 8 = ____
29. 80 ÷ 10 = ____
30. 7 ÷ 1 = ____
31. 45 ÷ 9 = ____
32. 48 ÷ 6 = ____
33. 5 ÷ 5 = ____
34. 30 ÷ 3 = ____
35. 16 ÷ 4 = ____
36. 72 ÷ 8 = ____
37. 10 ÷ 2 = ____
38. 1 ÷ 1 = ____
39. 54 ÷ 9 = ____
40. 21 ÷ 7 = ____
41. 25 ÷ 5 = ____
42. 15 ÷ 3 = ____
43. 32 ÷ 4 = ____
44. 24 ÷ 8 = ____
45. 90 ÷ 10 = ____
46. 18 ÷ 3 = ____
47. 63 ÷ 9 = ____
48. 54 ÷ 6 = ____
49. 45 ÷ 5 = ____
50. 6 ÷ 1 = ____
51. 20 ÷ 4 = ____
52. 49 ÷ 7 = ____
53. 15 ÷ 5 = ____
54. 0 ÷ 3 = ____
55. 28 ÷ 4 = ____
56. 30 ÷ 6 = ____
57. 16 ÷ 2 = ____
58. 21 ÷ 3 = ____
59. 81 ÷ 9 = ____
60. 64 ÷ 8 = ____
61. 30 ÷ 5 = ____
62. 12 ÷ 3 = ____
63. 27 ÷ 9 = ____
64. 42 ÷ 7 = ____
65. 40 ÷ 10 = ____
66. 10 ÷ 1 = ____
67. 24 ÷ 4 = ____
68. 18 ÷ 6 = ____
69. 35 ÷ 5 = ____
70. 27 ÷ 3 = ____
71. 72 ÷ 9 = ____
72. 42 ÷ 6 = ____

Name

PATH to FLUENCY Patterns With 10s, 5s, and 9s

These multiplication tables help us see some patterns that make recalling basic multiplications easier.

5s and 10s

×	1	2	3	4	5	6	7	8	9	10
1	1	2	3	4	5	6	7	8	9	10
2	2	4	6	8	10	12	14	16	18	20
3	3	6	9	12	15	18	21	24	27	30
4	4	8	12	16	20	24	28	32	36	40
5	5	10	15	20	25	30	35	40	45	50
6	6	12	18	24	30	36	42	48	54	60
7	7	14	21	28	35	42	49	56	63	70
8	8	16	24	32	40	48	56	64	72	80
9	9	18	27	36	45	54	63	72	81	90
10	10	20	30	40	50	60	70	80	90	100

9s

×	1	2	3	4	5	6	7	8	9	10
1	1	2	3	4	5	6	7	8	9	10
2	2	4	6	8	10	12	14	16	18	20
3	3	6	9	12	15	18	21	24	27	30
4	4	8	12	16	20	24	28	32	36	40
5	5	10	15	20	25	30	35	40	45	50
6	6	12	18	24	30	36	42	48	54	60
7	7	14	21	28	35	42	49	56	63	70
8	8	16	24	32	40	48	56	64	72	80
9	9	18	27	36	45	54	63	72	81	90
10	10	20	30	40	50	60	70	80	90	100

1. What pattern do you see in the 10s count-bys?

____

2. Look at the 5s and the 10s together. What patterns do you see?

____

3. Look at the 9s count-bys. How does each 9s count-by relate to the 10s count-by in the next row?

____

How could this pattern help you remember the 9s count-bys?

____

____

4. Look at the digits in each 9s product. What is the sum of the digits in each 9s product?

____

How could you use this knowledge to check your answers when you multiply by 9?

____

PATH to FLUENCY Patterns With Other Numbers

On these grids, find patterns with 2s, 4s, 6s, and 8s.

5 Look at the ones digits in all the 2s, 4s, 6s, and 8s count-bys. What pattern do you see?

____

6 Are the 2s, 4s, 6s, and 8s products even numbers or odd numbers?

____

2s, 4s, 6s, 8s

×	1	2	3	4	5	6	7	8	9
1	1	2	3	4	5	6	7	8	9
2	2	4	6	8	10	12	14	16	18
3	3	6	9	12	15	18	21	24	27
4	4	8	12	16	20	24	28	32	36
5	5	10	15	20	25	30	35	40	45
6	6	12	18	24	30	36	42	48	54
7	7	14	21	28	35	42	49	56	63
8	8	16	24	32	40	48	56	64	72
9	9	18	27	36	45	54	63	72	81
10	10	20	30	40	50	60	70	80	90

On the multiplication table labeled Doubles, look for rows that have products that are double the products in other rows.

7 Name the factors that have products that are double the products of another factor.

____

____

____

____

Doubles

×	1	2	3	4	5	6	7	8	9
1	1	2	3	4	5	6	7	8	9
2	2	4	6	8	10	12	14	16	18
3	3	6	9	12	15	18	21	24	27
4	4	8	12	16	20	24	28	32	36
5	5	10	15	20	25	30	35	40	45
6	6	12	18	24	30	36	42	48	54
7	7	14	21	28	35	42	49	56	63
8	8	16	24	32	40	48	56	64	72
9	9	18	27	36	45	54	63	72	81
10	10	20	30	40	50	60	70	80	90

8 How can you find 6 × 8 if you know 3 × 8?

____

Rewrite each list so that the count-by list is correct.

9 4, 8, 12, 18, 20, 24, 28 _______________

10 18, 28, 36, 45, 54, 63, 70 _______________

Check Understanding

Cross out the number that does not belong in this count-by list: 16, 24, 28, 32, 40, 48, 56, 64, 72.

Name ___________________________________

Math and Recipes

The animal keepers at zoos feed and care for the animals. The animal keepers consult a zoo nutritionist to decide what and how much to feed the animals. In the zoo kitchens there are recipes posted for each type of animal such as the one shown below.

Gorilla's Zoo Stew

32 carrots	8 yams
32 oranges	8 eggs
24 apples	16 bananas
64 ounces Monkey's Chow	72 grapes
48 ounces primate-diet food	56 stalks of celery
8 heads lettuce, any variety	bales of hydroponic grass to taste

Toss all ingredients lightly. Divide among 8 trays.

The recipe makes 8 gorilla servings.

Write an equation and solve the problem.

1. How much of each ingredient is in 1 gorilla serving?

____

____

____

____

2. How much of each ingredient in the Gorilla's Zoo Stew recipe is needed to serve 6 gorillas?

____

____

____

____

Favorite Zoo Animals

The students in third grade took a field trip to a zoo. The students were asked to name their favorite zoo animal. The pictograph below shows the animals the students chose.

Favorite Zoo Animal

Bear	☺ ☺ ☺ ☺ ☺ ☺ ☺
Elephant	☺ ☺ ☺ ☺ ☺ ☺ ☺ ☺
Giraffe	☺ ☺ ☺ ☺
Gorilla	☺ ☺ ☺ ☺ ☺ ☺
Lion	☺ ☺

Each ☺ stands for 7 students.

3. Use the information in the pictograph to complete the chart to show the number of students that chose each zoo animal.

Favorite Zoo Animal

Zoo Animal	Number of Students
Bear	
Elephant	
Giraffe	
Gorilla	
Lion	

Solve.

4. If 63 students chose a zebra as their favorite zoo animal, how many symbols would you use to show that on the pictograph?

____

Name _______________ Date _______________

Play a Target Game

The object of this target game is to score 100 points, or as close to 100 points as possible without going over.

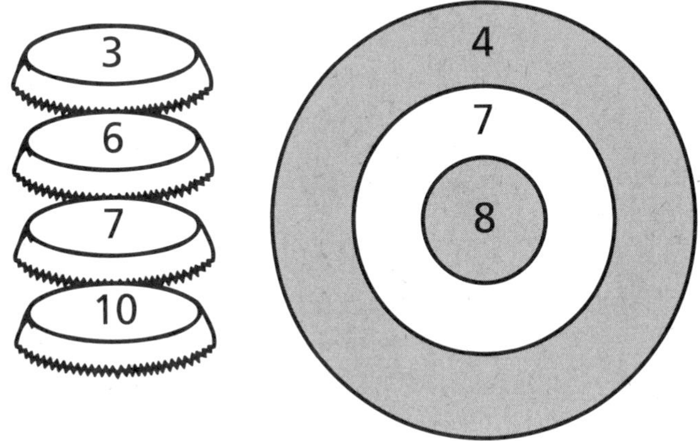

- You may drop two, three, or four bottle caps onto the target. To calculate the points for each drop, multiply the points on the cap by the points on the ring. For example, if the 3 cap lands on the 4 ring, the score would be $3 \times 4 = 12$.
- To find your final score, add the points for all your drops.

  Example: If the 3 bottle cap lands on the 4 ring, and the 7 bottle cap lands on the 8 ring, you could calculate your score using this equation.

  $(3 \times 4) + (7 \times 8) =$

  $12 \quad + \quad 56 \quad = 68$
- Repeat the process by tossing other caps. Keep track of your scores and your equations for finding your scores.

Name ________________________ Date ____________

1. What is the best possible score you can get with 2 bottle caps? Show your work.

2. How do you know that you found the best possible score with 2 caps? What strategy did you use?

3. What are two different scores you could get with the same 3 caps? Show your work.

4. Can you score exactly 100 points with 3 caps? Show your work. Show your work.

5. Michael says that he can score exactly 100 points with 4 bottle caps. Is that true? Show your work.

Estimada familia:

Su niño está participando en actividades matemáticas que le servirán para comprender el valor posicional, el redondeo y la suma, resta y multiplicación de números mayores.

- **Dibujos de valor posicional:** Los estudiantes aprenden a representar números por medio de dibujos que muestran cuántas centenas, decenas y unidades contienen. Las centenas están representadas con casillas, las decenas con segmentos verticales, llamados palitos de decenas, y las unidades con círculos pequeños. Los dibujos también se usan para ayudar a los estudiantes a comprender cómo se reagrupa en la suma y en la resta. Este es un dibujo de valor posicional para el número 178.

1 centena 7 decenas 8 unidades

Los palitos de decenas y los círculos se agrupan en grupos de 5 para que las cantidades se puedan ver más fácilmente y se eviten errores.

- **Tarjetas de código secreto:** Las tarjetas de código secreto son un conjunto de tarjetas con centenas, decenas y unidades. Los estudiantes aprenden acerca del valor posicional organizando las tarjetas de manera que muestren números de dos y de tres dígitos. Así se puede formar el número 148:

Estimar sumas y diferencias: Los estudiantes aprenden a estimar sumas y diferencias redondeando números. También usan las estimaciones para comprobar que sus respuestas son razonables.

	Redondear a la centena más próxima	Redondear a la decena más próxima
493	500	490
129	100	130
+ 369	+ 400	+ 370
991	Estimación: 1,000	Estimación: 990

Métodos de suma: Los estudiantes pueden usar el método común de EE. UU., conocido como Grupos nuevos arriba, y otros dos métodos alternativos. En el método de Grupos nuevos abajo, los estudiantes suman de derecha a izquierda y escriben la nueva decena y la nueva centena en el renglón. En el método de Mostrar todos los totales, los estudiantes suman en cualquier dirección, escriben sumas parciales y luego las suman para obtener el total. Los estudiantes también usan dibujos de comprobación para demostrar cómo se agrupan 10 unidades para formar una nueva decena, y 10 decenas para formar una nueva centena.

El método de Grupos nuevos abajo muestra el número 13 mejor que el método de Grupos nuevos arriba, en el que se separan los números 1 y 3. Además, es más fácil sumar con Grupos nuevos abajo, donde se suman los dos números que se ven y simplemente se añade 1.

Grupos nuevos arriba:

```
  1  ← la decena nueva
 46
+37
 83
```

Grupos nuevos abajo:

```
 46
+37   ← la decena nueva
  1
 83
```

Sumar de derecha a izquierda.

Mostrar todos los totales:

```
 46
+37
 70
 13   ← la decena nueva
 83
```

Sumar de izquierda a derecha.

Dibujo de comprobación:

8 decenas 3 unidades

la decena nueva

Métodos de resta: Los estudiantes pueden usar el método común de EE. UU., en el cual la resta se hace de derecha a izquierda, desagrupando antes de restar cada columna. También aprenden un método alternativo en el que desagrupan todo *antes* de restar. Si los estudiantes desagrupan todo primero, pueden restar de izquierda a derecha o de derecha a izquierda.

El método de Desagrupar primero ayuda a los estudiantes a evitar el error común de restar un número pequeño de arriba, de un número más grande de abajo.

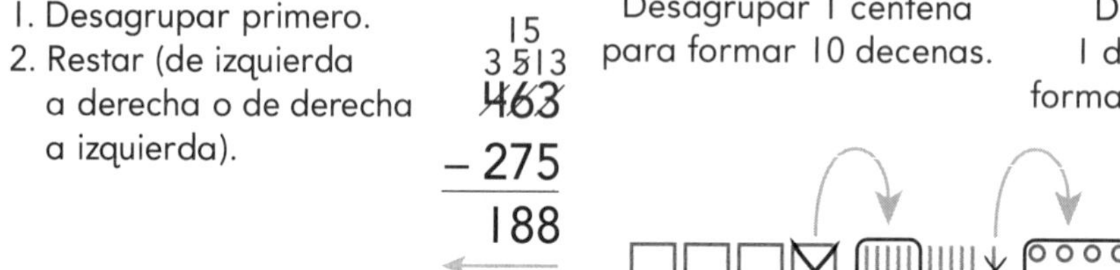

3 centenas 15 decenas 13 unidades

Si tiene alguna pregunta o algún comentario, por favor comuníquese conmigo. Gracias.

Atentamente,
El maestro de su niño

compatible numbers

expanded form

equal (=)

greatest

estimate

hundreds

A number written to show the value of each of its digits.

Examples:

347 = 300 + 40 + 7

347 = 3 hundreds + 4 tens + 7 ones

Numbers that are easy to compute mentally. Compatible numbers can be used to check if answers are reasonable.

Example:

692 + 234

Some compatible numbers for the addends are 700 and 200 or 700 and 234.

56 29 64

64 is the greatest number.

A symbol used to compare two amounts or values. It shows that what is on the left of the sign is equal to or the same value as what is on the right of the sign.

Example:

3,756 = 3,756

3,756 *is equal* to 3,756.

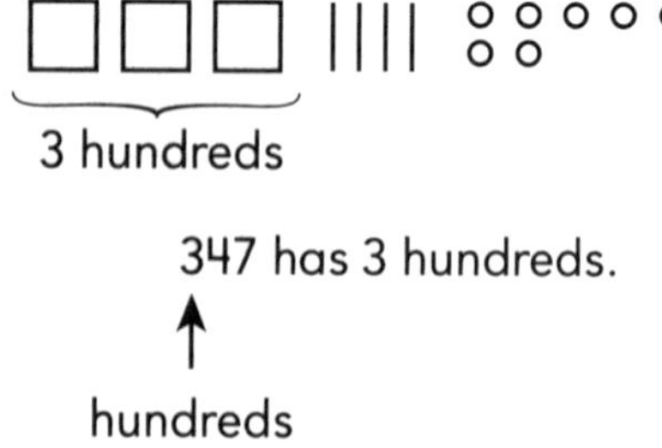

A reasonable guess about how many or about how much.

hundred thousands

ones

input-output table

place value

least

round

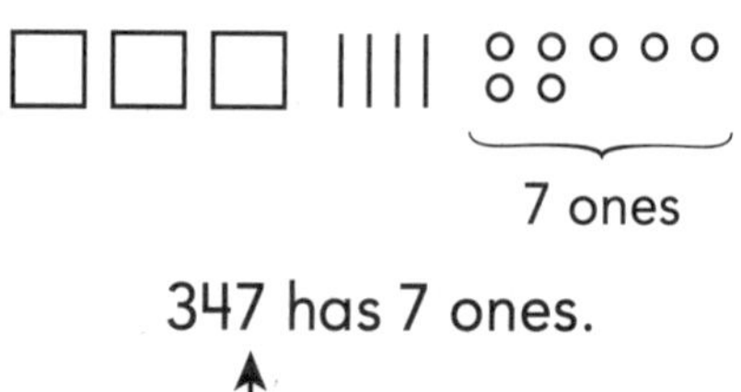

347 has 7 ones.

↑

ones

Hundred Thousands	Ten Thousands	Thousands	Hundreds	Tens	Ones
5	4	6	7	8	2

There are 5 hundred thousands in 546,782.

The value assigned to the place that a digit occupies in a number.

9	6	2
↑	↑	↑
hundreds	tens	ones

A table that displays ordered pairs of numbers that follow a specific rule.

Example:

Rule: Add 4	
Input	**Output**
3	7
5	9
9	13
11	15
15	19

To find about how many or how much by expressing a number to the nearest ten, hundred, thousand, and so on.

72 41 89

41 is the least number.

standard form

thousands

tens

unit square

ten thousands

Hundred Thousands	Ten Thousands	Thousands	Hundreds	Tens	Ones
5	4	6	7	8	2

There are 6 thousands in 546,782.

The name of a number written using digits.

Example:
1,829

A square whose area is 1 square unit.

4 tens

347 has 4 tens.

tens

Hundred Thousands	Ten Thousands	Thousands	Hundreds	Tens	Ones
5	4	6	7	8	2

There are 4 ten thousands in 546,782.

1

1

2

2

10

10

20

20

3

3

4

4

30

30

40

40

5

5

6

6

50

50

60

60

7

7

8

8

70

70

80

80

9

9

90

90

100

100

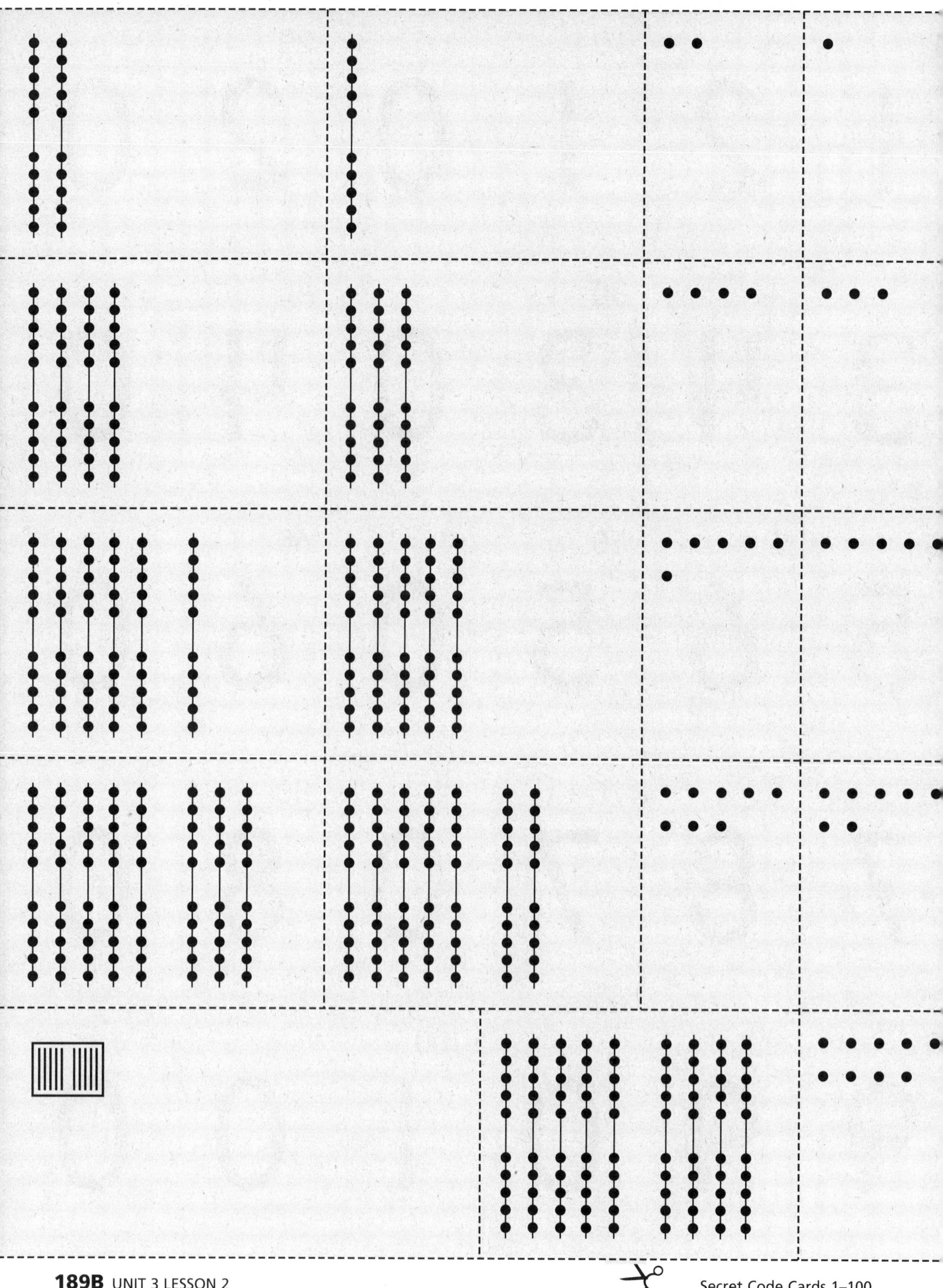

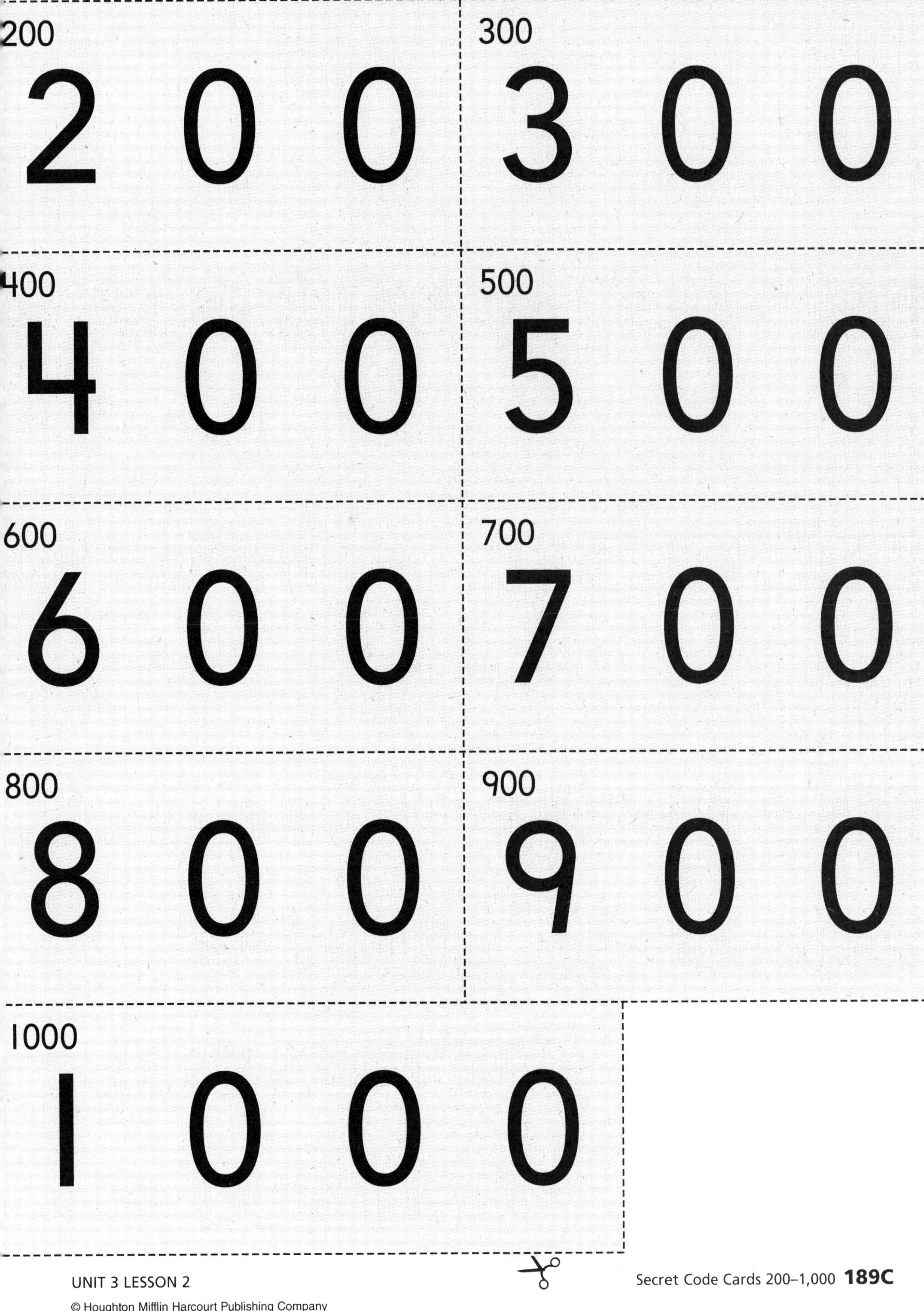
200
2 0 0
300
3 0 0
400
4 0 0
500
5 0 0
600
6 0 0
700
7 0 0
800
8 0 0
900
9 0 0
1000
1 0 0 0

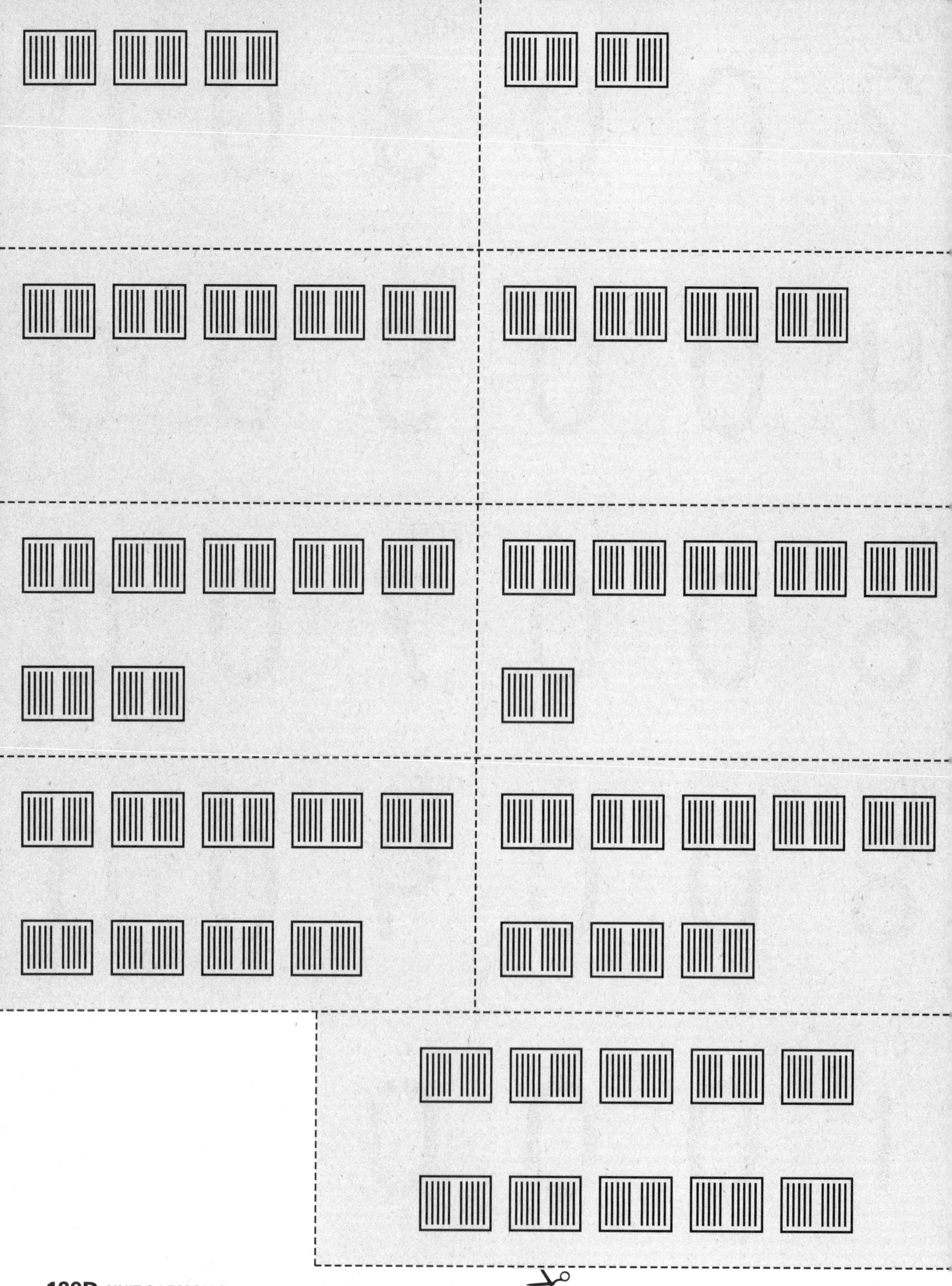

Name ______________________

VOCABULARY
hundreds
tens
ones
thousands
expanded form

Build and Discuss Other Numbers

Write the number.

1. 700 + 20 + 9 = ________

2. 1,000 + 600 + 80 + 4 = ________

3. 400 + 5 = ________

4. 3 **hundreds** + 4 **tens** + 7 **ones** = ________

5. 8 hundreds + 1 ten = ________

6. 1 **thousand** + 9 hundreds + 1 ten + 8 ones = ________

Write the number in expanded form in two ways.

7. 585

____

____

8. 1,367

____

____

9. 213

____

____

What's the Error?

Dear Math Students,

I was asked to build the number 238 with Secret Code Cards. I made the number with these cards.

200 3 8

2 0 0 | 3 | 8

200 3 8

2 3 8

My teacher says that what I showed is not correct. Can you help me?

Your friend,

Puzzled Penguin

10 Write an answer to Puzzled Penguin.

____

____

____

____

Check Understanding

Use the number 456 to complete the sentences. Build the number with Secret Code Cards to check your answer.

The value of the digit 4 is ________.

The value of the digit 5 is ________.

The value of the digit 6 is ________.

Name ______________________________

Reasonable Answers

Use rounding to decide if the answer is reasonable. Write your estimate. Write *yes* or *no* for the reasonableness of the answer.

24. 93 − 29 = 64

25. 113 + 57 = 140

26. 83 + 19 = 102

27. 336 + 258 = 594

28. 468 − 158 = 280

29. 437 + 149 = 536

30. 725 − 285 = 590

31. 249 + 573 = 822

32. 542 − 167 = 475

What's the Error?

Dear Math Students,

Today my teacher asked me to estimate the answer to this problem:

Ms. Smith's class brought in 384 cans for the food drive. Mr. Alvarez's class brought in 524 cans. About how many cans did the two classes bring in?

$$\begin{array}{r} 384 \\ +\ 524 \\ \hline \end{array} \quad \longrightarrow \quad \begin{array}{r} 300 \\ +\ 500 \\ \hline 800 \end{array}$$

About 800 cans were brought in.

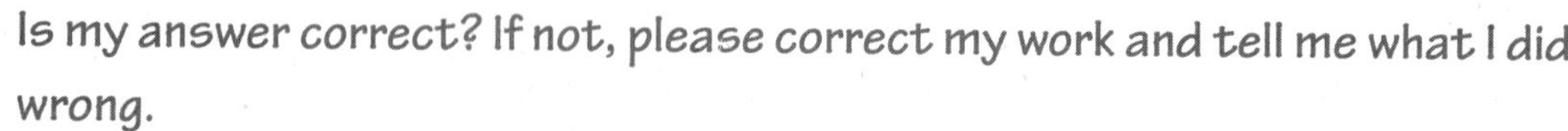

Is my answer correct? If not, please correct my work and tell me what I did wrong.

Your friend,
Puzzled Penguin

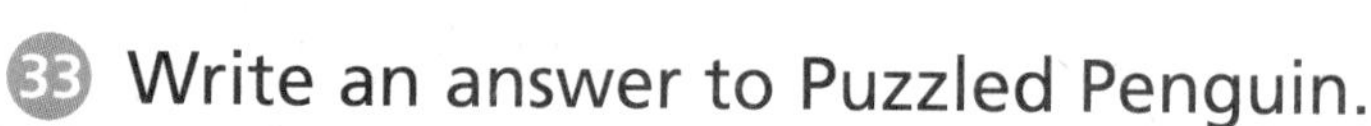

33 Write an answer to Puzzled Penguin.

Estimate the Number of Objects

Jar D has 100 Beans. Estimate how many beans are in the other jars.

34 Jar A ____________

35 Jar B ____________

36 Jar C ____________

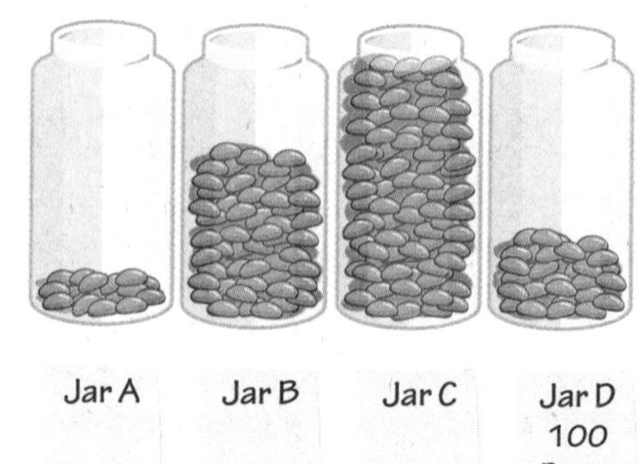

Check Understanding

Round each number to the nearest ten.

83 ________ 98 ________ 245 ________ 362 ________

Name ______________________

Decide When to Group

Decide which new groups you will make.
Then add to see if you were correct.

1. $\begin{array}{r} 123 \\ +\ 247 \\ \hline \end{array}$

2. $\begin{array}{r} 358 \\ +\ 434 \\ \hline \end{array}$

3. $\begin{array}{r} 732 \\ +\ 189 \\ \hline \end{array}$

4. $\begin{array}{r} 416 \\ +\ 396 \\ \hline \end{array}$

Add.

5. $\begin{array}{r} 647 \\ +\ 178 \\ \hline \end{array}$

6. $\begin{array}{r} 132 \\ +\ 763 \\ \hline \end{array}$

7. $\begin{array}{r} 554 \\ +\ 257 \\ \hline \end{array}$

8. $\begin{array}{r} 168 \\ +\ 692 \\ \hline \end{array}$

9. $\begin{array}{r} 384 \\ +\ 586 \\ \hline \end{array}$

10. $\begin{array}{r} 631 \\ +\ 189 \\ \hline \end{array}$

11. $\begin{array}{r} 464 \\ +\ 446 \\ \hline \end{array}$

12. $\begin{array}{r} 313 \\ +\ 649 \\ \hline \end{array}$

13. 576 + 265 = ______

14. 568 + 219 = ______

15. 389 + 511 = ______

16. 137 + 284 = ______

Write an equation and solve the problem.

17. The first animated film at the movie theatre lasted 129 minutes. The second film lasted 104 minutes. How many minutes in all did the two movies last?

____

Solve and Discuss

Write an equation and solve the problem.

Show your work.

18 Jacob has 347 basketball cards in his collection. He has 256 baseball cards. How many cards does he have altogether?

____

19 Jasmine's family drove for two days to visit her grandparents. They drove 418 miles on the first day and 486 miles on the second day. How many miles did they drive in all?

____

20 The florist ordered 398 roses and 562 tulips. How many flowers did the florist order in all?

____

21 The suitcase that Emilio packed weighed 80 pounds. His wife packed three suitcases. Each of her suitcases weighed 30 pounds. How many pounds in all did their suitcases weigh?

____

22 Write and solve an addition word problem where 287 and 614 are addends.

____

____

____

Check Understanding

Explain how you know when you need to group when adding two 3-digit numbers.

Name ______________________________

PATH to FLUENCY

Discuss Subtraction Methods

Solve this word problem.

Mr. Kim had 134 kites in his hobby store. He sold 58 of them. How many kites does he have now?

1. Write a subtraction that you could do to answer this question.

   ____

2. Make a place value drawing for 134. Take away 58. How many are left?

3. Write a numerical solution method for what you did in the drawing.

4. Describe how you ungrouped to subtract.

   ____

   ____

   ____

   ____

   ____

What's the Error?

Dear Math Students,

Today I found the answer to 134 − 58, but I don't know if I did it correctly. Please look at my work. Is my answer right? If not, please correct my work and tell what I did wrong.

$$\begin{array}{r} 134 \\ -\ 58 \\ \hline 124 \end{array}$$

Your friend,
Puzzled Penguin

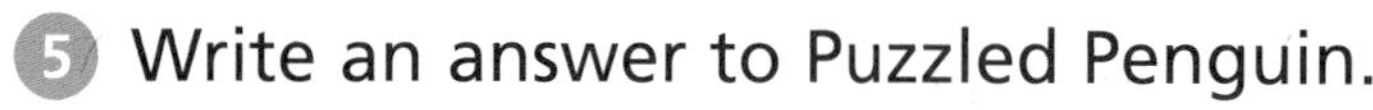

5 Write an answer to Puzzled Penguin.

____

____

PATH to FLUENCY
Subtraction Detective

To avoid making subtraction mistakes, look at the top number closely. Do all the ungrouping *before* you subtract. The magnifying glass around the top number helps you remember to be a "subtraction detective."

Subtract. Show your ungroupings numerically and with proof drawings.

6 $\begin{array}{r} 371 \\ -\ 86 \\ \hline \end{array}$

7 $\begin{array}{r} 163 \\ -\ 47 \\ \hline \end{array}$

8 $\begin{array}{r} 459 \\ -175 \\ \hline \end{array}$

Check Understanding

Complete. Always subtract the ______________ number from the ______________ number.

Name ______________________________

PATH to FLUENCY

Practice Subtracting Across Zeros

Subtract. Make proof drawings for Exercises 7–10.

7. $\begin{array}{r} 800 \\ -\ 391 \\ \hline \end{array}$

8. $\begin{array}{r} 500 \\ -\ 333 \\ \hline \end{array}$

9. $\begin{array}{r} 400 \\ -\ 217 \\ \hline \end{array}$

10. $\begin{array}{r} 900 \\ -\ 818 \\ \hline \end{array}$

11. $\begin{array}{r} 600 \\ -\ 575 \\ \hline \end{array}$

12. $\begin{array}{r} 700 \\ -\ 248 \\ \hline \end{array}$

13. $\begin{array}{r} 200 \\ -\ 109 \\ \hline \end{array}$

14. $\begin{array}{r} 800 \\ -\ 519 \\ \hline \end{array}$

15. **Math Journal** Write a word problem that is solved by subtracting a 2-digit number from a 3-digit number that has a zero in both the ones and tens places. Then solve the problem.

PATH to FLUENCY

Practice Deciding When to Ungroup

Subtract. Make proof drawings if you need to on MathBoards or on a separate sheet of paper.

16. 912 − 265

17. 323 − 147

18. 280 − 136

19. 489 − 263

20. $\begin{array}{r} 754 \\ -\ 389 \\ \hline \end{array}$

21. $\begin{array}{r} 912 \\ -\ 437 \\ \hline \end{array}$

22. $\begin{array}{r} 341 \\ -\ 178 \\ \hline \end{array}$

23. $\begin{array}{r} 603 \\ -\ 464 \\ \hline \end{array}$

Check Understanding

Subtract. 300 – 156. Make a proof drawing to show that your answer is correct.

Name ____________________

PATH to FLUENCY

Ungroup from Left or Right

Tony and Maria each solved this problem:

On Tuesday morning, a bookstore had 463 copies of a new bestseller. By the end of the day, 275 copies were sold. How many copies were left?

Tony

Tony started ungrouping from the left.

1. He has enough hundreds.
2. He does not have enough tens. He ungroups 1 hundred to make 10 more tens.

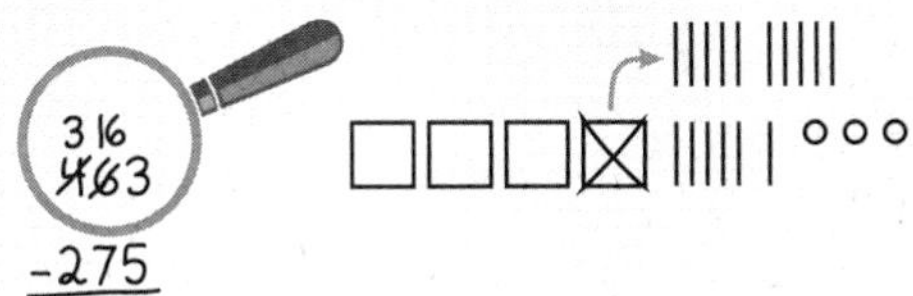

3. He does not have enough ones. He ungroups 1 ten to make 10 more ones.

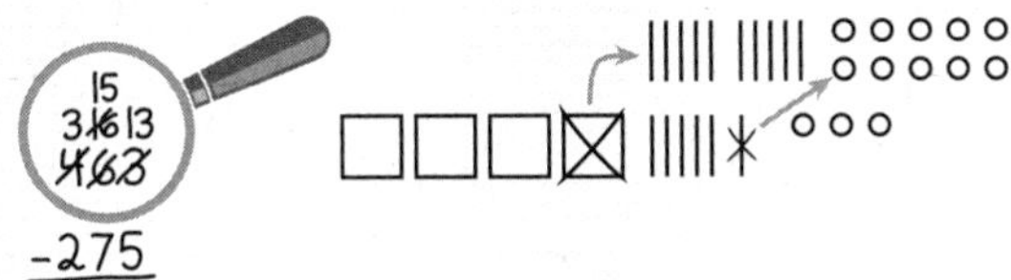

4. Complete the subtraction.

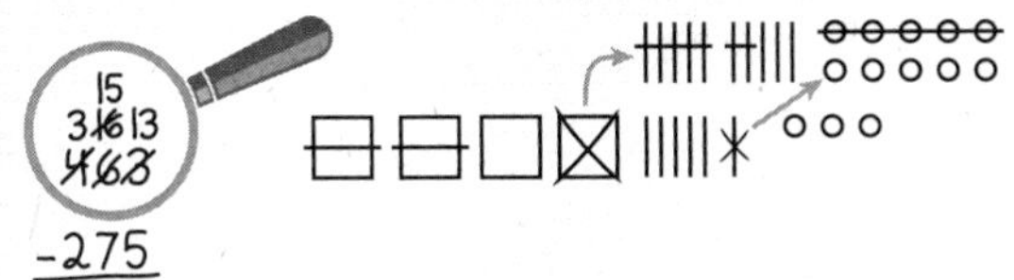

Maria

Maria started ungrouping from the right.

1. She does not have enough ones. She ungroups 1 ten to make 10 more ones.

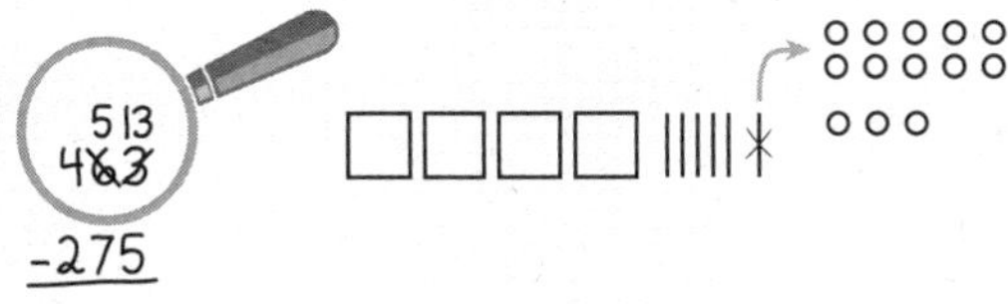

2. She does not have enough tens. She ungroups 1 hundred to get 10 more tens.

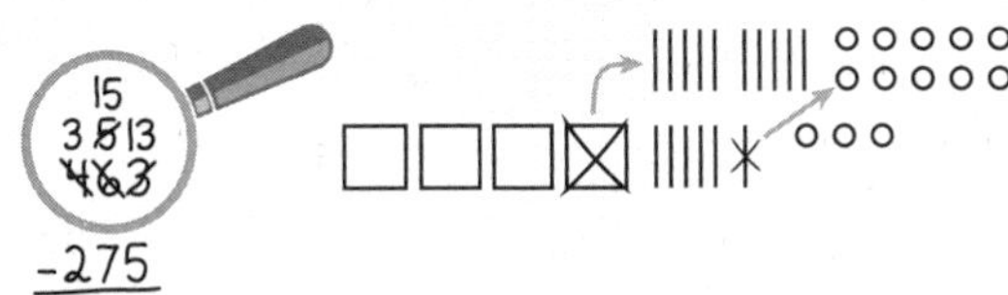

3. She has enough hundreds.
4. Complete the subtraction.

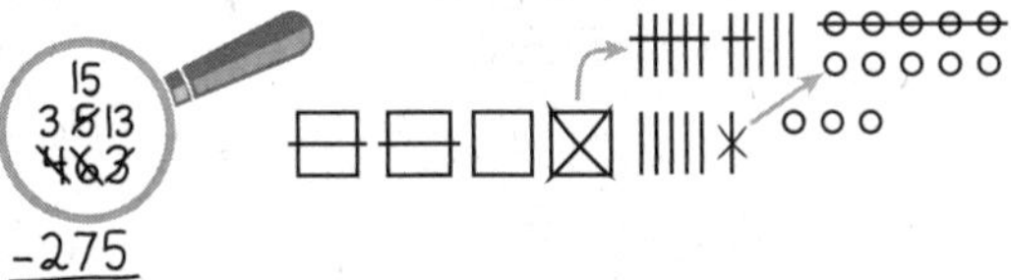

PATH to FLUENCY Choose a Method to Subtract

Subtract.

1. 686 − 387

2. 340 − 167

3. 765 − 498

4. 841 − 253

5. 912 − 575

6. 853 − 194

7. 705 − 429

8. 998 − 299

9. 513 − 156

10. 627 − 348

11. 544 − 169

12. 810 − 261

Solve.

13. Rory is putting 302 digital photos in an album. Of these, 194 are from her trip to Florida. How many photos are not from Rory's trip?

14. There were 645 bike riders in a race. Toby finished eighty-seventh. How many riders finished after Toby?

Check Understanding

Explain two subtraction methods—ungrouping from the left and ungrouping from the right.

 Name ______________________

Subtract and Check

Solve each problem.

Show your work.

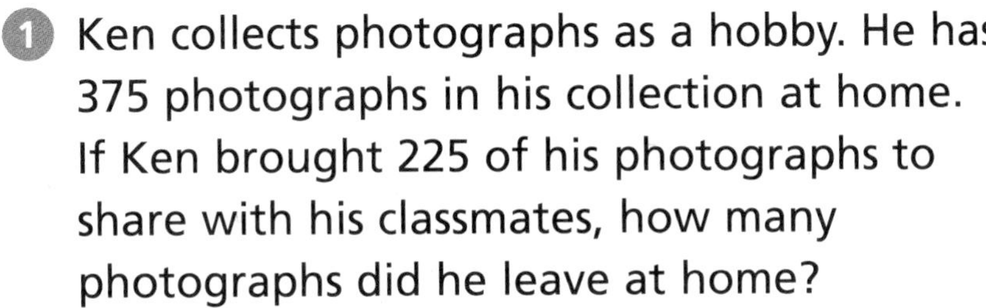

1. Ken collects photographs as a hobby. He has 375 photographs in his collection at home. If Ken brought 225 of his photographs to share with his classmates, how many photographs did he leave at home?

____

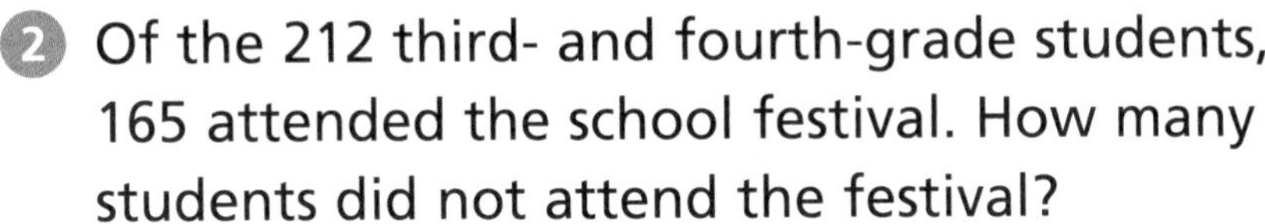

2. Of the 212 third- and fourth-grade students, 165 attended the school festival. How many students did not attend the festival?

____

3. Becky has 653 marbles in her collection. Riley has 438 marbles in her collection. How many more marbles does Becky have than Riley?

____

4. Andrea and John need 750 tickets to get a board game. They have 559 tickets. How many more tickets do they need?

____

PATH to FLUENCY Practice Deciding When to Ungroup

Answer each question.

Adair subtracted 595 from 834.

5. Did she have to ungroup to make more tens? Explain.

6. Did she have to ungroup to make more ones? Explain.

Beatrice subtracted 441 from 950.

7. Did she have to ungroup to make more tens? Explain.

8. Did she have to ungroup to make more ones? Explain.

Wan subtracted 236 from 546.

9. Did he have to ungroup to make more tens? Explain.

10. Did he have to ungroup to make more ones? Explain.

Check Understanding

Explain how to decide when to ungroup in a subtraction problem.

Name ______________________________

PATH to FLUENCY

Practice Addition and Subtraction

Add or subtract.

1. $\begin{array}{r} 112 \\ +\ 459 \\ \hline \end{array}$

2. $\begin{array}{r} 572 \\ -\ 357 \\ \hline \end{array}$

3. $\begin{array}{r} 253 \\ +\ 328 \\ \hline \end{array}$

4. $\begin{array}{r} 710 \\ -\ 464 \\ \hline \end{array}$

5. $\begin{array}{r} 461 \\ -\ 182 \\ \hline \end{array}$

6. $\begin{array}{r} 540 \\ +\ 175 \\ \hline \end{array}$

7. $\begin{array}{r} 921 \\ -\ 653 \\ \hline \end{array}$

8. $\begin{array}{r} 398 \\ -\ 99 \\ \hline \end{array}$

9. $\begin{array}{r} 712 \\ +\ 189 \\ \hline \end{array}$

10. $\begin{array}{r} 600 \\ -\ 223 \\ \hline \end{array}$

11. $\begin{array}{r} 809 \\ -\ 576 \\ \hline \end{array}$

12. $\begin{array}{r} 634 \\ +\ 287 \\ \hline \end{array}$

Solve.

13. The height of Angeline Falls in Washington is 450 feet. Snoqualmie Falls in Washington is 182 feet lower than Angeline Falls. What is the height of Snoqualmie Falls?

____

14. Jill scored 534 points at the arcade on Friday night. She scored 396 points on Saturday night. How many points did she score altogether?

____

Solve Real World Problems

The students at Liberty Elementary collected pennies for a fundraiser.

Pennies Collected					
Grade	1	2	3	4	5
Number of Pennies	225	436	517	609	342

Write an equation and solve the problem.

Show your work.

15 How many pennies did Grades 2 and 5 collect?

____

16 How many more pennies did Grades 1 and 3 together collect than Grade 4?

____

17 Is the total number of pennies collected by Grades 1 and 4 greater than or less than the total number collected by Grades 3 and 5?

____

18 The total number of pennies collected by which three grades equals about 900?

____

19 The Kindergarten students collected 198 fewer pennies than the Grade 3 students. How many pennies did the Kindergarteners collect?

____

Check Understanding

Describe a real world situation in which you would need to add or subtract.

Name ______________________

Solve Word Problems with Greater Numbers

Solve each problem. Then use compatible numbers to check your answer.

Show your work.

10. Jenna has $250 in a bank account. After her birthday she adds $135 to the account. Then the next week, she takes out $40 to buy a game for her computer. How much money is in the account now?

____

11. Alex and his father each have a collection of sports cards. Alex's father has 900 cards and Alex has 350 fewer cards than his father. After Alex's friend gives Alex 72 more cards, how many does Alex have?

____

12. A truck has 2,600 cans of tomatoes to deliver to stores. The first store takes 450 cans. How many cans of tomatoes are left on the truck?

____

13. There are 1,250 people living in Union. There are 2,100 more people living in Grantville than in Union. What is the population of Grantville?

____

14. Valley View Farm grew 2,549 pounds of potatoes during the summer. The Valley View Farm store sold 1,083 pound of potatoes. How many pounds of potatoes were left?

____

Solve Word Problems with Greater Numbers (continued)

Solve each problem. Then use compatible numbers to check your answer for reasonableness.

Show your work.

15. The PTA has $3,029 in its account to pay for school field trips. A field trip costs $576. If the PTA pays for the field trip, how much will be left in the account? Is your answer reasonable? Explain.

16. The Scott family is taking a trip to Washington, D.C. which is 1,395 miles from their home. So far they have driven 612 miles. How many more miles do they need to drive? Is your answer reasonable? Explain.

17. Last week 5,089 books were checked out from the city library. There were 4,962 books returned last week. How many more books were checked out than returned? Is your answer reasonable? Explain.

Check Understanding

Describe how you decide whether an answer is reasonable or not.

 Name ______________________

Math and Maps

The Pony Express was a mail service from St. Joseph, Missouri, to Sacramento, California. The Pony Express service carried mail by horseback riders in relays.

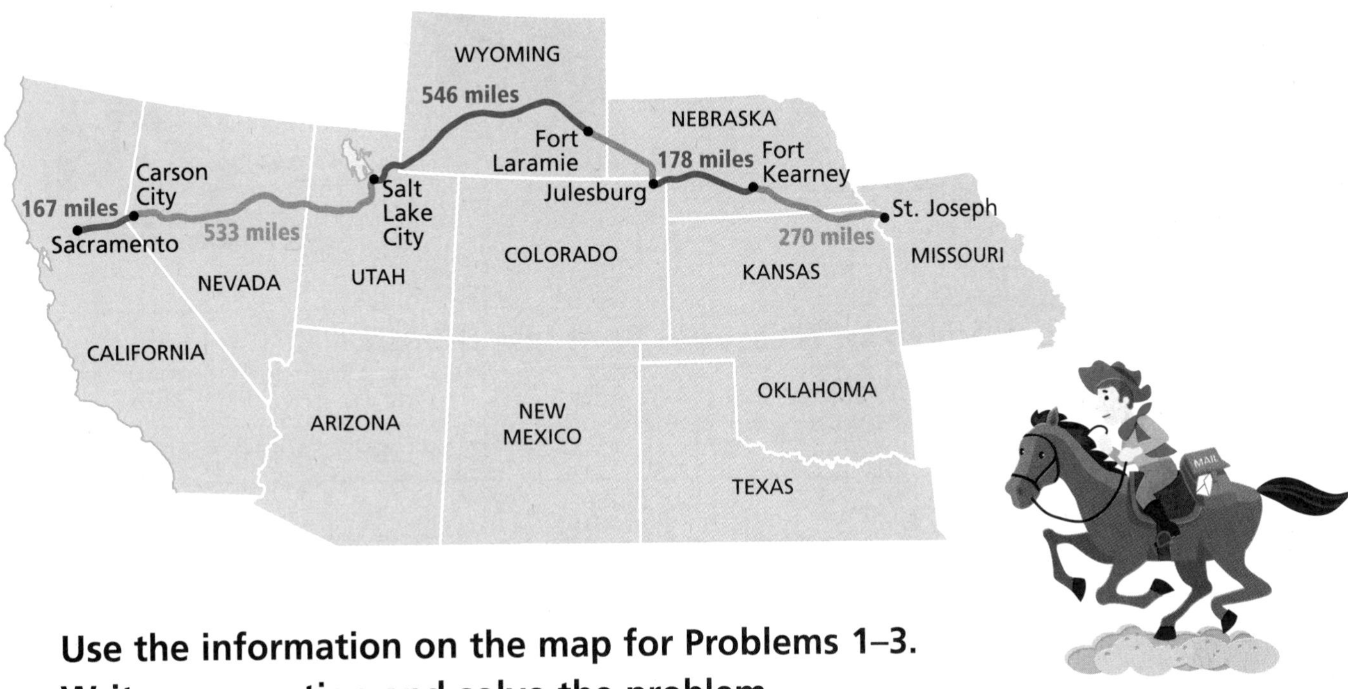

Use the information on the map for Problems 1–3. Write an equation and solve the problem.

1. How many miles did the Pony Express riders travel on a trip from Sacramento to Salt Lake City?

____

2. The total distance from St. Joseph to Fort Laramie is 616 miles. How many miles is it from Julesburg to Fort Laramie?

____

3. Write and solve a problem that can be answered using the map.

____

____

Use a Table

It took the Pony Express 10 days to deliver letters between Sacramento and St. Joseph. Today we send text messages that are delivered within a few seconds. The chart below shows the number of messages sent in a month by different students.

Number of Messages Sent last Month					
Name	Robbie	Samantha	Ellen	Bryce	Callie
Number	528	462	942	388	489

Use the information in the table for Problems 4–6. Write an equation and solve the problem.

4. How many more messages did Robbie send than Callie?

5. How many more messages did Ellen send than Bryce and Samantha combined?

6. Tamara said that Robbie and Bryce together sent 806 messages. Is that number reasonable? Explain. Then find the actual number to see if you are correct.

Name ______________________________

Identify Place Value Through Hundred Thousands

VOCABULARY
hundred thousands
ten thousands

Write each number in the place-value chart.

1. 12,072
2. 6,908
3. 90,542
4. 175,163

	Hundred Thousands	Ten Thousands	Thousands	Hundreds	Tens	Ones
1.						
2.						
3.						
4.						

Write the value of the underlined digit.

5. 13,456 ____________
6. 190,765 ____________
7. 88,763 ____________
8. 4,567 ____________
9. 25,783 ____________
10. 95,426 ____________

Write Numbers Different Ways

Write each number in standard form.

11. sixty thousand, one hundred eight ____________
12. one hundred sixty-six thousand, eighty ____________

Write each number in word form.

13. 17,893 ______________________________
14. 175,635 ______________________________

Write each number in expanded form.

15. 23,059 ______________________________
16. 103,814 ______________________________

More and Less

Write the number that is 10,000 more and the number that is 10,000 less.

17 87,630 10,000 more ________ 10,000 less ________

18 19,455 10,000 more ________ 10,000 less ________

Write the number that is 1,000 more and the number that is 1,000 less.

19 5,176 1,000 more ________ 1,000 less ________

20 26,709 1,000 more ________ 1,000 less ________

Write the number that is 100 more and the number that is 100 less.

21 2,547 100 more ________ 100 less ________

22 30,169 100 more ________ 100 less ________

What's the Error?

Dear Math Students,

Today my teacher asked me to find the number that is 1,000 more than 15,319, but I don't know if my answer is correct. I wrote:

1,000 more than 15,319 is 25,319.

Your friend,
Puzzled Penguin

23 Write an answer to Puzzled Penguin.

____

____

____

____

Name ______________________________

Compare and Order Numbers Through Hundred Thousands

VOCABULARY
greatest
least

Discuss the problem below.

Jim has 24 trading cards and Hattie has 42 trading cards. Who has more trading cards? How do you know?

Write greater than (>), less than (<), or equal (=) to make each statement true.

24 3,989 ◯ 3,899

25 2,385 ◯ 2,385

26 3,235 ◯ 2,350

27 4,008 ◯ 4,108

28 2,563 ◯ 2,563

29 8,567 ◯ 9,765

30 23,836 ◯ 7,859

31 5,206 ◯ 52,026

32 89,748 ◯ 98,478

33 12,904 ◯ 12,904

34 14,538 ◯ 41,830

35 61,564 ◯ 60,569

Write each group of numbers in order from greatest to least.

36 8,456 4,567 4,675

____

37 3,465 3,654 3,546

____

38 8,091 10,981 9,081

____

39 13,230 11,710 5,608

____

40 30,714 32,740 30,174

____

41 89,518 85,981 89,815

____

42 Fremont has a population of 26,397. Hastings has a population of 24,907. Which city has the greater population?

____

43 Bella, Jason, and Nico each took a car trip over the summer. Bella traveled 3,208 miles. Jason traveled 4,796 miles. Nico traveled 958 miles. Who traveled the greatest distance?

____

Rounding with Greater Numbers

Round each number to the nearest ten thousand.

44. 87,630 ________
45. 46,433 ________
46. 34,641 ________
47. 27,309 ________

Round each number to the nearest thousand.

48. 1,380 ________
49. 5,998 ________
50. 41,632 ________
51. 65,594 ________

Round to the place of the underlined digit.

52. <u>1</u>4,594 ________
53. 2<u>4</u>,596 ________
54. 23,<u>3</u>07 ________
55. 4,<u>1</u>36 ________

Estimate with Greater Numbers

Round each number to the greatest place to estimate each sum or difference.

56. $\begin{array}{r} 2{,}491 \\ +\ 1{,}309 \\ \hline \end{array}$

57. $\begin{array}{r} 7{,}463 \\ -\ 3{,}270 \\ \hline \end{array}$

58. $\begin{array}{r} 65{,}594 \\ -\ 12{,}407 \\ \hline \end{array}$

59. $\begin{array}{r} 20{,}365 \\ +\ 18{,}679 \\ \hline \end{array}$

Check Understanding

How is rounding 46,037 to the nearest ten thousand like rounding 482 to the nearest hundred?

Name ______________________________

Model a Product of Ones and Tens

VOCABULARY
unit square

The number of **unit squares** in an array of connected unit squares is the area of the rectangle formed by the squares. We sometimes just show the measurement of length and width.

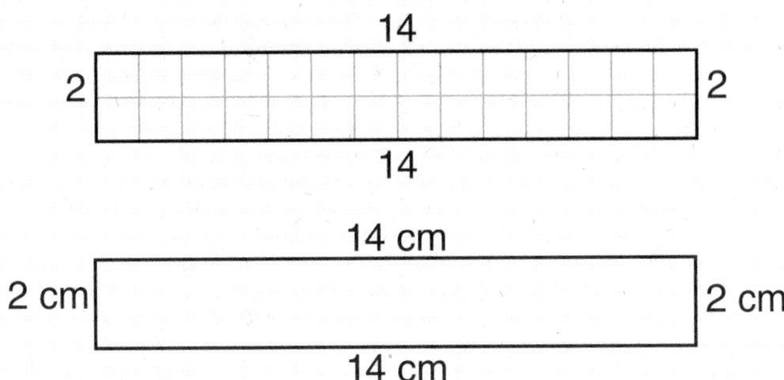

You can draw a rectangle for any multiplication. In the real world, we use multiplication for finding both sizes of arrays and areas of figures.

A 2×14 rectangle has 28 unit squares inside, so $2 \times 14 = 28$.

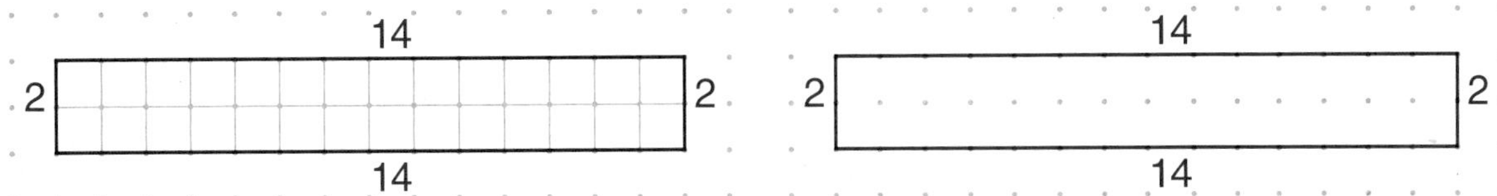

1. On your MathBoard, draw a 14×2 rectangle. How is the 14×2 rectangle similar to the 2×14 rectangle? How is it different?

____

____

____

____

2. How do the areas of the 2×14 and 14×2 rectangles compare?

____

Factor the Tens to Multiply Ones and Tens

This 3×40 rectangle contains 12 groups of 10 square units, so its area is 120 square units.

	40 = 10	+ 10	+ 10	+ 10	
1	$1 \times 10 = 10$	$1 \times 10 = 10$	$1 \times 10 = 10$	$1 \times 10 = 10$	1
1	$1 \times 10 = 10$	$1 \times 10 = 10$	$1 \times 10 = 10$	$1 \times 10 = 10$	1
1	$1 \times 10 = 10$	$1 \times 10 = 10$	$1 \times 10 = 10$	$1 \times 10 = 10$	1
	10	+ 10	+ 10	+ 10	

3. How can we show this numerically? Complete the steps.

$3 \times 40 = (3 \times 1) \times (\_\_\_\_ \times 10)$

$= (\_\_\_\_ \times \_\_\_\_) \times (1 \times 10)$

$= \_\_\_\_ \times 10 = 120$

4. On your MathBoard, draw a 40×3 rectangle and find its area.

____

5. How is the 40×3 rectangle similar to the 3×40 rectangle? How is it different?

____

____

____

____

6. Write out the steps for finding 4×30 by factoring the tens. Use your MathBoard if you need to.

____

____

____

Name ______________________________

Explore the Area Model

Copy this rectangle on your MathBoard.

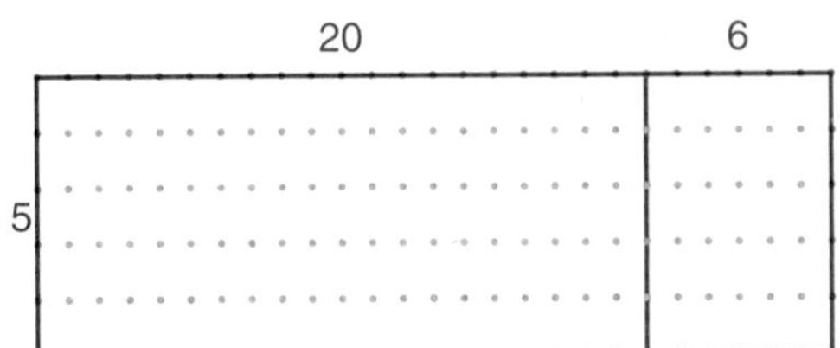

7. How many square units of area are there in the tens part of the drawing? ____________

8. What multiplication equation gives the area of the tens part of the drawing? ____________ Write this equation in its rectangle.

9. How many square units of area are there in the ones part of the drawing? ____________

10. What multiplication equation gives the area of the ones part? ____________ Write this equation in its rectangle.

11. What is the total of the two areas? ____________

12. How do you know that 130 is the correct product of 5×26?

____

____

13. **Read Problems A and B.**

A. Brad's photo album has 26 pages. Each page has 5 photos. How many photos are in Brad's album?

B. Nick took 5 photos. Haley took 26 photos. How many more photos did Haley take than Nick?

Which problem could you solve using the multiplication you just did? Explain why.

____

____

Use Rectangles to Multiply

Draw a rectangle for each problem on your MathBoard. Find the tens product, the ones product, and the total.

14. 8×38

15. 3×29

16. 4×28

17. 7×34

18. 2×38

19. 3×28

20. 5×30

21. 5×28

Solve each problem.

22. Lucille put 9 rows of tile on her mudroom floor. Each row has 16 tiles. How many tiles are on Lucille's mudroom floor?

Show your work.

23. A pizzeria can make pizzas on thin crusts, thick crusts, or flatbreads. The pizzeria has a total of 57 different ways to top the pizzas. How many different combinations of crusts and pizza toppings can the pizzeria make?

24. Complete this word problem. Then solve it.

_______ has ____ boxes of _______.

There are ____ _______ in each box.

How many _______ does _______

have altogether? _______

Name ____________________

Multiply 1-Digit Numbers by Hundreds

You can use an area model to multiply a 1-digit number by a 3-digit number.

$3 \times 249 = \square$

249 =	200	40	9
3	$3 \times 200 = 600$	$3 \times 40 = 120$	$3 \times 9 = 27$

1. What two operations are used to find the product of 3×249 using the area model?

   ____________________ ____________________

2. What multiplication equation gives the area of the hundreds part of the model? ____________________

3. What multiplication equation gives the area of the tens part of the model? ____________________

4. What multiplication equation gives the area of the ones part of the model? ____________________

5. What is the total of the three areas? ____________________

PATH to FLUENCY Use an Area Model to Solve

For each acre of land that a farmer cuts, he gets 127 bales of hay. The farmer cuts his land 4 times every year. What is the total number of bales of hay the farmer will get from each acre this year?

6. Draw rectangles to represent the problem.

7. Explain how to use the area model to solve the problem above.

____

____

____

8. Use your rectangle drawing and the steps you described to find the answer to the problem.

____

Write the equation.

9. If the farmer has 9 acres of land, how many bales of hay will the farmer cut each year? Complete the area model to find the answer.

Equation: ____________________

Name ______________________ Date ______________

Raise Money

The students at Kevin's school are collecting pennies for a service project. They plan to use the money to buy flowers to plant at a local park. They need 1,000 pennies to buy each flat of flowers.

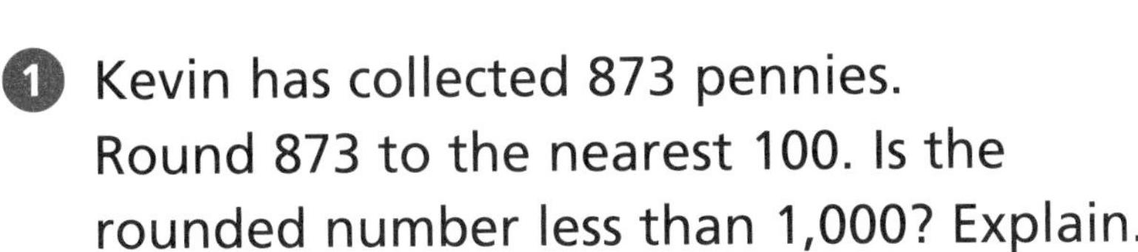

1. Kevin has collected 873 pennies. Round 873 to the nearest 100. Is the rounded number less than 1,000? Explain.

2. What would you have to add to 873 to get 1,000? How do you know your answer is reasonable?

3. Write an addition word problem related to Problem 2. Explain how the problems are related.

 Name Date

4 June, Ella, and Joshua also are collecting pennies for the service project. June collected 324 pennies, Ella collected 442 pennies, and Joshua collected 248 pennies.

Part A

Estimate to decide whether these three students collected enough pennies to buy a flat of flowers.

Part B

Find the actual answer to check if you are correct. Explain your strategy.

Part C

How many more pennies do the students need to collect to buy a second flat of flowers? Show your work.

Part D

Write an addition word problem related to Part C. Explain how the problems are related.

Halves and Fourths in Measurement

Fractions in Measurement

Halves	Quarters
Length	

Money	
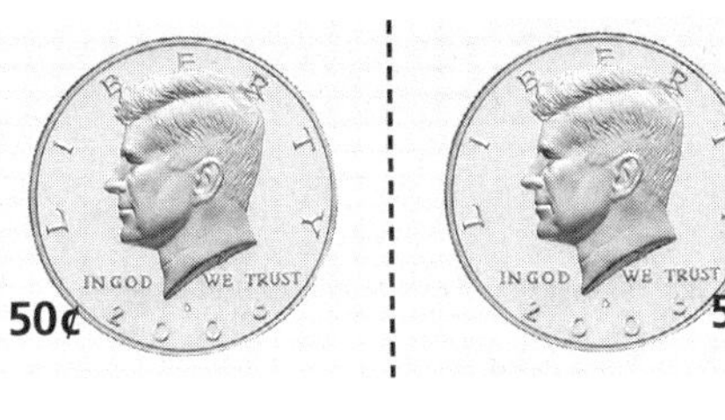 Half-Dollar Half-Dollar	 4 Quarters
Time	
 30 minutes + 30 minutes = 60 minutes = 1 hour	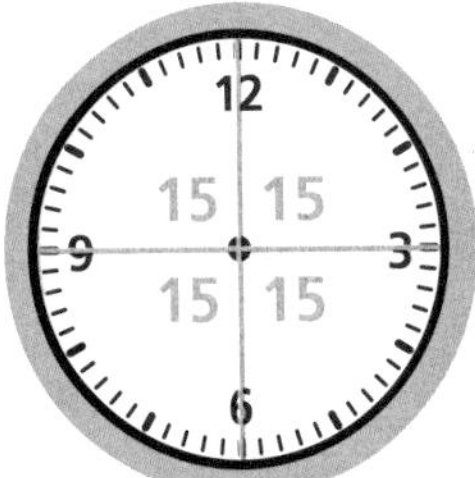 15 minutes + 15 minutes + 15 minutes + 15 minutes = 60 minutes = 1 hour
Liquid Capacity	
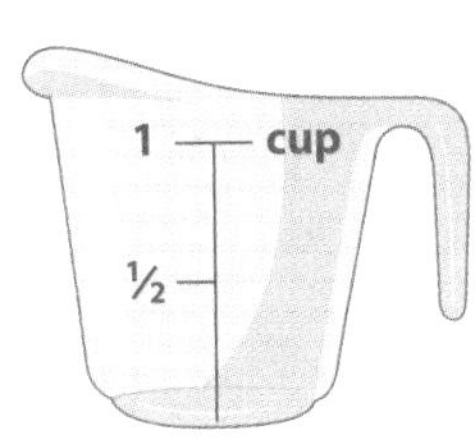	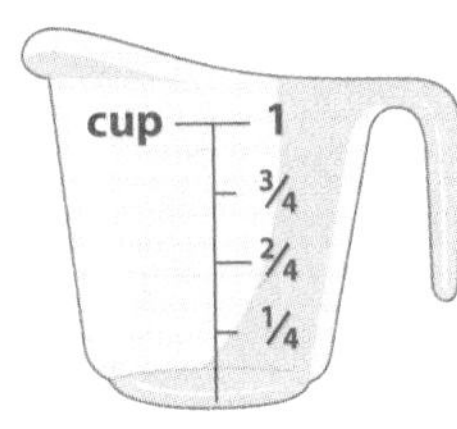

Measures and Units of Time

Table of Measures

Metric	Customary
Length/Area	
1 meter (m) = 10 decimeters (dm) 1 meter (m) = 100 centimeters (cm) 1 decimeter (dm) = 10 centimeters (cm) 1 square centimeter = 1 cm^2 A metric unit for measuring area. It is the area of a square that is one centimeter on each side.	1 foot (ft) = 12 inches (in.) 1 yard (yd) = 3 feet (ft) 1 mile (mi) = 5,280 feet (ft) 1 square inch = 1 in^2 A customary unit for measuring area. It is the area of a square that is one inch on each side.
Liquid Volume	
1 liter (L) = 1,000 milliliters (mL)	1 tablespoon (tbsp) = $\frac{1}{2}$ fluid ounce (fl oz) 1 cup (c) = 8 fluid ounces (fl oz) 1 pint (pt) = 2 cups (c) 1 quart (qt) = 2 pints (pt) 1 gallon (gal) = 4 quarts (qt)

Table of Units of Time

Time	
1 minute (min) = 60 seconds (sec) 1 hour (hr) = 60 minutes 1 day = 24 hours 1 week (wk) = 7 days 1 month, about 30 days 1 year (yr) = 12 months (mo) or about 52 weeks	1 year = 365 days 1 leap year = 366 days

Properties of Operations	
Associative Property of Addition	
$(a + b) + c = a + (b + c)$	$(2 + 5) + 3 = 2 + (5 + 3)$
Commutative Property of Addition	
$a + b = b + a$	$4 + 6 = 6 + 4$
Identity Property of Addition	
$a + 0 = 0 + a = a$	$3 + 0 = 0 + 3 = 3$
Associative Property of Multiplication	
$(a \cdot b) \cdot c = a \cdot (b \cdot c)$	$(3 \cdot 5) \cdot 7 = 3 \cdot (5 \cdot 7)$
Commutative Property of Multiplication	
$a \cdot b = b \cdot a$	$6 \cdot 3 = 3 \cdot 6$
Identity Property of Multiplication	
$a \cdot 1 = 1 \cdot a = a$	$8 \cdot 1 = 1 \cdot 8 = 8$
Zero Property of Multiplication	
$a \cdot 0 = 0 \cdot a = 0$	$5 \cdot 0 = 0 \cdot 5 = 0$
Distributive Property of Multiplication over Addition	
$a \cdot (b + c) = (a \cdot b) + (a \cdot c)$	$2 \cdot (4 + 3) = (2 \cdot 4) + (2 \cdot 3)$

Addition and Subtraction Problem Types

	Result Unknown	Change Unknown	Start Unknown
Add to	Aisha had 274 stamps in her collection. Then her grandfather gave her 65 stamps. How many stamps does she have now? *Situation and solution equation:*[1] $274 + 65 = s$	Aisha had 274 stamps in her collection. Then her grandfather gave her some stamps. Now she has 339 stamps. How many stamps did her grandfather give her? *Situation equation:* $274 + s = 339$ *Solution equation:* $s = 339 - 274$	Aisha had some stamps in her collection. Then her grandfather gave her 65 stamps. Now she has 339 stamps. How many stamps did she have to start? *Situation equation* $s + 65 = 339$ *Solution equation:* $s = 339 - 65$
Take from	A store had 750 bottles of water at the start of the day. During the day, the store sold 490 bottles. How many bottles did they have at the end of the day? *Situation and solution equation:* $750 - 490 = b$	A store had 750 bottles of water at the start of the day. The store had 260 bottles left at the end of the day. How many bottles did the store sell? *Situation equation:* $750 - b = 260$ *Solution equation:* $b = 750 - 260$	A store had a number of bottles of water at the start of the day. The store sold 490 bottles of water. At the end of the day 260 bottles were left. How many bottles did the store have to start with? *Situation equation:* $b - 490 = 260$ *Solution equation:* $b = 260 + 490$

[1]A situation equation represents the structure (action) in the problem situation. A solution equation shows the operation used to find the answer.

Addition and Subtraction Problem Types (continued)

<table>
<tr><th></th><th>Total Unknown</th><th>Addend Unknown</th><th>Other Addends Unknown</th></tr>
<tr><td rowspan="3">Put Together/ Take Apart</td>
<td>A clothing store has 375 shirts with short sleeves and 148 shirts with long sleeves. How many shirts does the store have in all?

Math drawing:[1]

Situation and solution equation:
$375 + 148 = s$</td>
<td>Of the 523 shirts in a clothing store, 375 have short sleeves. The rest have long sleeves. How many shirts have long sleeves?

Math drawing:

Situation equation:
$523 = 375 + s$
Solution equation:
$s = 523 - 375$</td>
<td>A clothing store has 523 shirts. Some have short sleeves and 148 have long sleeves. How many of the shirts have short sleeves?

Math drawing:

Situation equation
$523 = s + 148$
Solution equation:
$s = 523 - 148$</td></tr>
<tr><td colspan="2" rowspan="2">Both Addends Unknown is a productive extension of this basic situation, especially for small numbers less than or equal to 10. Such take apart situations can be used to show all the decompositions of a given number. The associated equations, which have the total on the left of the equal sign, help students understand that the = sign does not always mean makes or results in but always does mean is the same number as.</td>
<th>Both Addends Unknown</th></tr>
<tr><td>A clothing store has 523 shirts. Some have short sleeves and some have long sleeves. Write a situation equation for how many shirts with long sleeves and how many shirts with short sleeves the store could have.

Math Drawing:

Situation Equation:
$523 = \square + \square$</td></tr>
</table>

[1]These math drawings are called math mountains in Grades 1–3 and break apart drawings in Grades 4 and 5.

Addition and Subtraction Problem Types (continued)

	Difference Unknown	Greater Unknown	Smaller Unknown
Compare	At a zoo, the female black bear weighs 175 pounds. The male black bear weighs 260 pounds. How much more does the male black bear weigh than the female black bear? At a zoo, the female black bear weighs 175 pounds. The male black bear weighs 260 pounds. How much less does the female black bear weigh than the male black bear? *Math drawing:* [260] [175] (d) *Situation equation:* $175 + d = 260$, or $d = 260 - 175$ *Solution equation:* $d = 260 - 175$	**Leading Language** At a zoo, the female black bear weighs 175 pounds. The male black bear weighs 85 pounds more than the female black bear. How much does the male black bear weigh? **Misleading Language** At a zoo, the female black bear weighs 175 pounds. The female black bear weighs 85 pounds less than the male black bear. How much does the male black bear weigh? *Math drawing:* [m] [175] (85) *Situation and solution equation:* $175 + 85 = m$	**Leading Language** At a zoo, the male black bear weighs 260 pounds. The female black bear weighs 85 pounds less than the male black bear. How much does the female black bear weigh? **Misleading Language** At a zoo, the male black bear weighs 260 pounds. The male black bear weighs 85 pounds more than the female black bear. How much does the female black bear weigh? *Math drawing:* [260] [f] (85) *Situation equation* $f + 85 = 260$, or $f = 260 - 85$ *Solution equation:* $f = 260 - 85$

A comparison sentence can always be said in two ways. One way uses *more*, and the other uses *fewer* or *less*. Misleading language suggests the wrong operation. For example, it says *the female black bear weighs 85 pounds less than the male*, but you have to add 85 pounds to the female's weight to get the male's weight.

Multiplication and Division Problem Types

	Product Unknown	Group Size Unknown	Number of Groups Unknown
Equal Groups	A teacher bought 5 boxes of markers. There are 8 markers in each box. How many markers did the teacher buy? *Math drawing:* 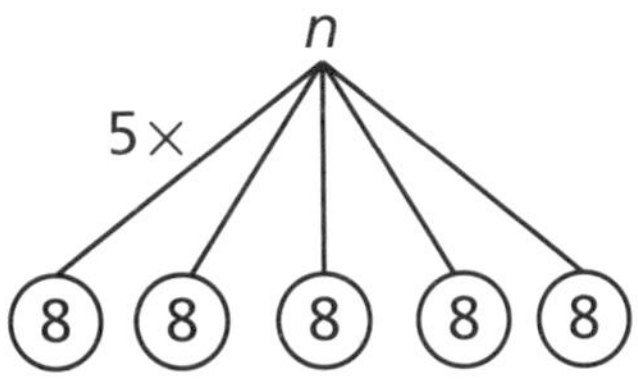 n $5\times$ 8 8 8 8 8 *Situation and solution equation:* $n = 5 \cdot 8$	A teacher bought 5 boxes of markers. She bought 40 markers in all. How many markers are in each box? *Math drawing:* 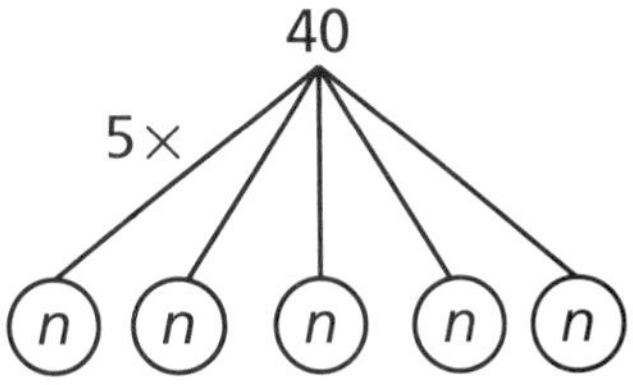 40 $5\times$ n n n n n *Situation equation:* $5 \cdot n = 40$ *Solution equation:* $n = 40 \div 5$	A teacher bought boxes of 8 markers. She bought 40 markers in all. How many boxes of markers did she buy? *Math drawing:* 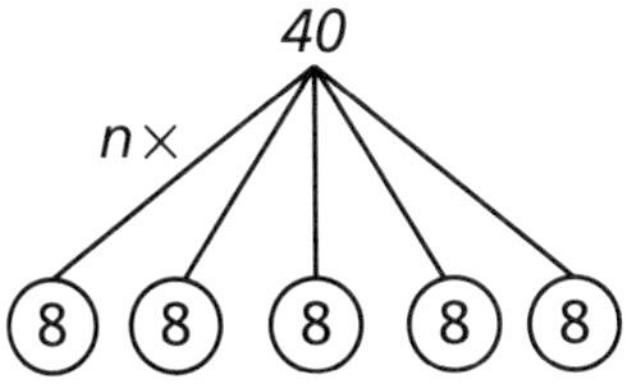 40 $n\times$ 8 8 8 8 8 *Situation equation* $n \cdot 8 = 40$ *Solution equation:* $n = 40 \div 8$

Multiplication and Division Problem Types (continued)

	Product Unknown	Factor Unknown	Factor Unknown
Arrays	For the yearbook photo, the drama club stood in 3 rows of 7 students. How many students were in the photo in all? *Math drawing:* 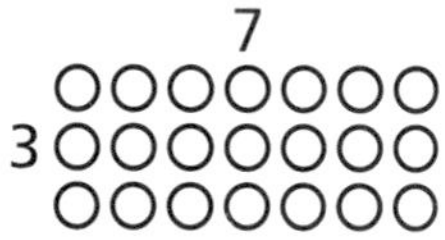 7 (across), 3 (down) OOOOOOO OOOOOOO OOOOOOO *Situation and solution equation:* $n = 3 \cdot 7$	For the yearbook photo, the 21 students in drama club stood in 3 equal rows. How many students were in each row? *Math drawing:* 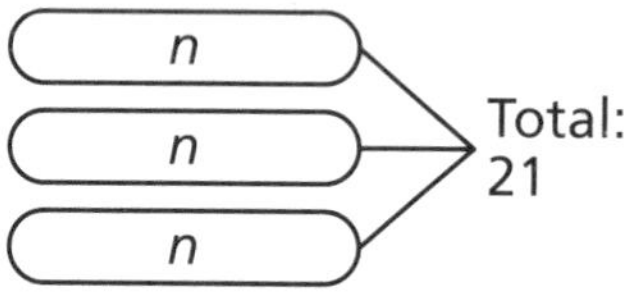 n, n, n → Total: 21 *Situation equation:* $3 \cdot n = 21$ *Solution equation:* $n = 21 \div 3$	For the yearbook photo, the 21 students in drama club stood in rows of 7 students. How many rows were there? *Math drawing:* 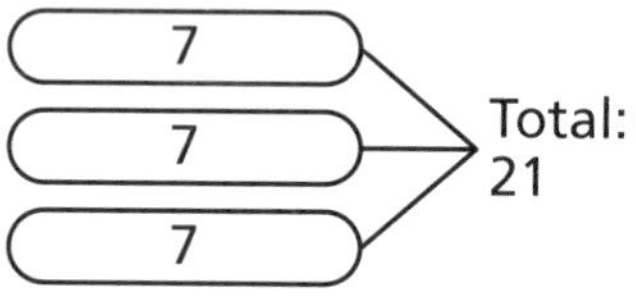 7, 7, 7 → Total: 21 *Situation equation* $n \cdot 7 = 21$ *Solution equation:* $n = 21 \div 7$
Area	The floor of the kitchen is 2 meters by 5 meters. What is the area of the floor? *Math drawing:* 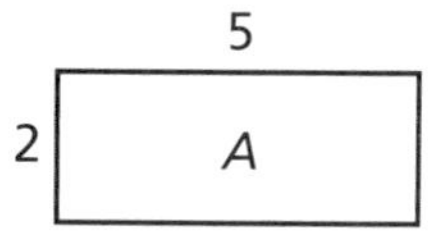 5 (top), 2 (side), A (inside) *Situation and solution equation:* $A = 5 \cdot 2$	The floor of the kitchen is 5 meters long. The area of the floor is 10 square meters. What is the width of the floor? *Math drawing:* 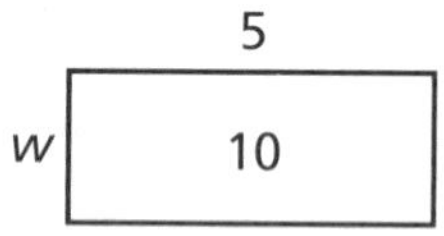 5 (top), w (side), 10 (inside) *Situation equation:* $5 \cdot w = 10$ *Solution equation:* $w = 10 \div 5$	The floor of the kitchen is 2 meters wide. The area of the floor is 10 square meters. What is the length of the floor? *Math drawing:* 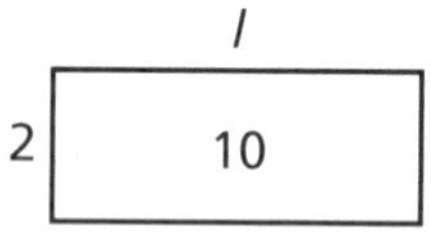 l (top), 2 (side), 10 (inside) *Situation equation* $l \cdot 2 = 10$ *Solution equation:* $l = 10 \div 2$

MathWord **Power**

Word Review 

Work with a partner. Choose a word from a current unit or a review word from a previous unit. Use the word to complete one of the activities listed on the right. Then ask your partner if they have any edits to your work or questions about what you described. Repeat, having your partner choose a word.

Activities

- Give the meaning in words or gestures.
- Use the word in a sentence.
- Give another word that is related to the word in some way and explain the relationship.

Crossword Puzzle  

Create a crossword puzzle similar to the example below. Use vocabulary words from the unit. You can add other related words, too. Challenge your partner to solve the puzzle.

<table>
<tr><td></td><td></td><td></td><td></td><td>1 s</td><td>u</td><td>m</td><td></td></tr>
<tr><td></td><td>2 a</td><td></td><td></td><td>u</td><td></td><td></td><td></td></tr>
<tr><td></td><td>d</td><td></td><td></td><td>b</td><td></td><td></td><td></td></tr>
<tr><td>3 a</td><td>d</td><td>d</td><td>i</td><td>t</td><td>i</td><td>o</td><td>4 n</td></tr>
<tr><td></td><td>e</td><td></td><td></td><td>r</td><td></td><td></td><td>u</td></tr>
<tr><td></td><td>n</td><td></td><td></td><td>a</td><td></td><td></td><td>m</td></tr>
<tr><td>5 a</td><td>d</td><td>d</td><td></td><td>c</td><td></td><td></td><td>b</td></tr>
<tr><td></td><td></td><td></td><td></td><td>t</td><td></td><td></td><td>e</td></tr>
<tr><td></td><td></td><td></td><td></td><td>i</td><td></td><td></td><td>r</td></tr>
<tr><td>6 r</td><td>e</td><td>g</td><td>r</td><td>o</td><td>u</td><td>p</td><td></td></tr>
<tr><td></td><td></td><td></td><td></td><td>n</td><td></td><td></td><td></td></tr>
</table>

Across

1. The answer to an addition problem
3. __________ and subtraction are operations that undo each other.
5. To put amounts together
6. When you trade 10 ones for 1 ten, you __________.

Down

1. The operation that you can use to find out how much more one number is than another
2. In 24 + 65 = 89, 24 is an _____.
4. A combination of the digits 0, 1, 2, 3, 4, 5, 6, 7, 8, and 9

Vocabulary Activities

Word Wall  

With your teacher's permission, start a word wall in your classroom. As you work through each lesson, put the math vocabulary words on index cards and place them on the word wall. You can work with a partner or a small group choosing a word and giving the definition.

Word Web 

Make a word web for a word or words you do not understand in a unit. Fill in the web with words or phrases that are related to the vocabulary word.

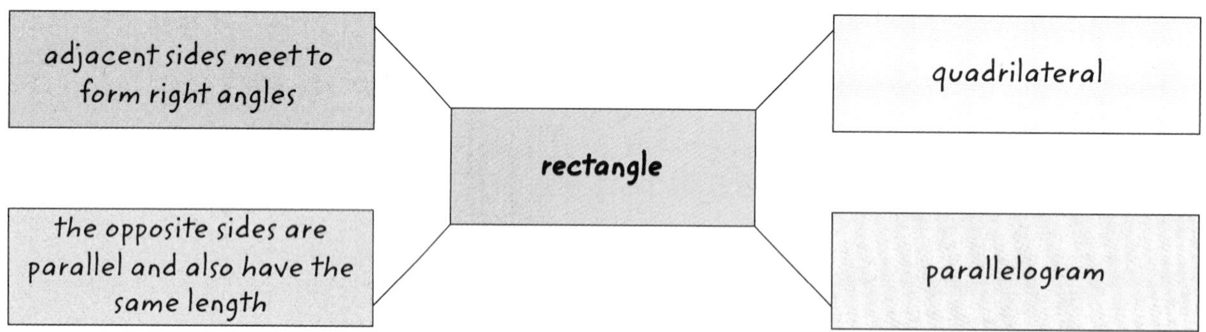

Alphabet Challenge  

Take an alphabet challenge. Choose three letters from the alphabet. Think of three vocabulary words for each letter. Then write the definition or draw an example for each word.

A	D	L
addition	data	liter
array	denominator	line segment
area	divide	line plot

Concentration 

Write the vocabulary words and related words from a unit on index cards. Write the definitions on a different set of index cards. Choose 3 to 6 pairs of vocabulary words and definitions. Mix up the set of pairs. Then place the cards facedown on a table. Take turns turning over two cards. If one card is a word and one card is a definition that matches the word, take the pair. Continue until each word has been matched with its definition.

Math Journal 

As you learn new words, write them in your Math Journal. Write the definition of the word and include a sketch or an example. As you learn new information about the word, add notes to your definition.

polygon: a closed plane figure with sides made of straight line segments.

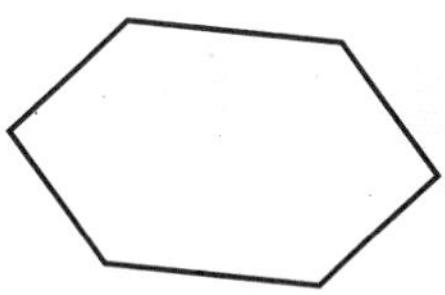

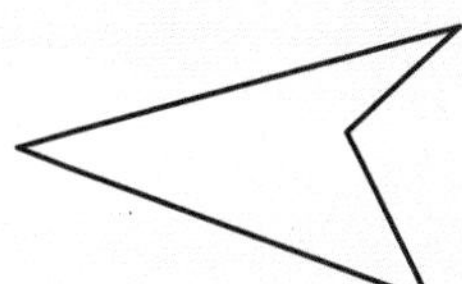

In concave polygons, there exists a line segment with endpoints inside the polygon and a point on the line segment that is outside the polygon.

What's the Word? 

Work together to make a poster or bulletin board display of the words in a unit. Write definitions on a set of index cards. Mix up the cards. Work with a partner, choosing a definition from the index cards. Have your partner point to the word on the poster and name the matching math vocabulary word. Switch roles and try the activity again.

the bottom number in a fraction that shows the total number of equal parts in the whole

fraction
unit fraction
denominator
numerator
equivalent
equivalent fractions
equivalence chain
thirds
fourths
eighths
halves
sixths

A

addend
One of two or more numbers to be added together to find a sum.

Example:

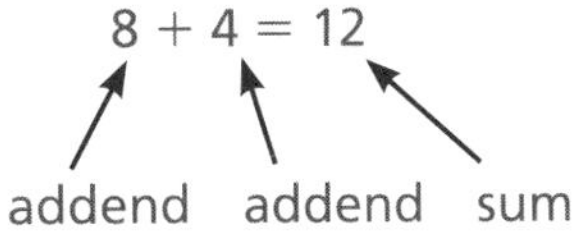

addition
A mathematical operation that combines two or more numbers.

Example:

23 + 52 = 75

addend addend sum

adjacent sides
Two sides of a figure that meet at a point.

Example:
Sides *a* and *b* are adjacent.

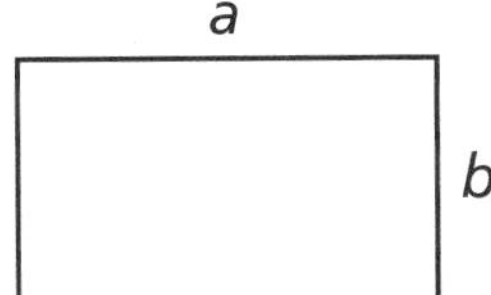

A.M.
The time period between midnight and noon.

analog clock
A clock with a face and hands.

angle
A figure formed by two rays or two line segments that meet at an endpoint.

area
The total number of square units that cover a figure.

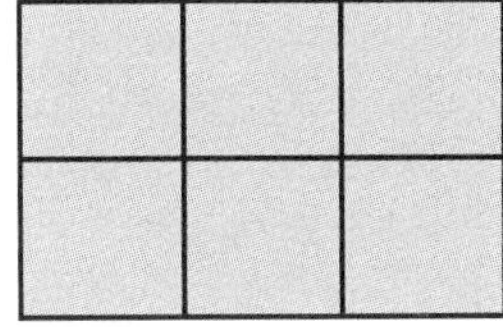

Example:
The area of the rectangle is 6 square units.

array
An arrangement of objects, pictures, or numbers in columns and rows.

Associative Property of Addition (Grouping Property of Addition)
The property that states that changing the way in which addends are grouped does not change the sum.

Example:

$(2 + 3) + 1 = 2 + (3 + 1)$

$5 + 1 = 2 + 4$

$6 = 6$

Associative Property of Multiplication (Grouping Property of Multiplication)

The property that states that changing the way in which factors are grouped does not change the product.

Example:

$(2 \times 3) \times 4 = 2 \times (3 \times 4)$

$6 \times 4 = 2 \times 12$

$24 = 24$

axis (plural: axes)

A reference line for a graph. A graph has two axes; one is horizontal and the other is vertical.

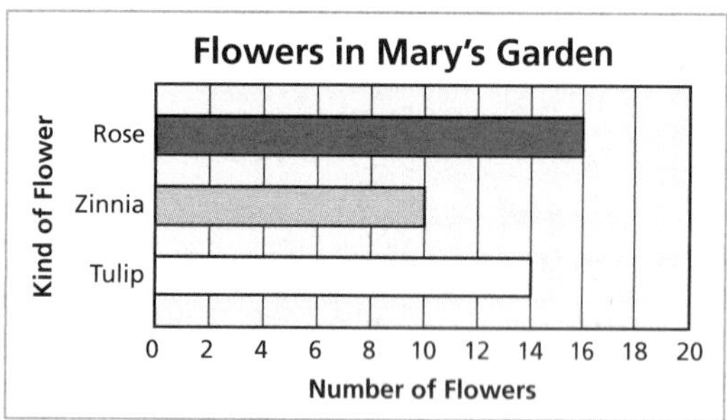

B

bar graph

A graph that uses bars to show data. The bars may be horizontal, as in the graph above, or vertical, as in the graph below.

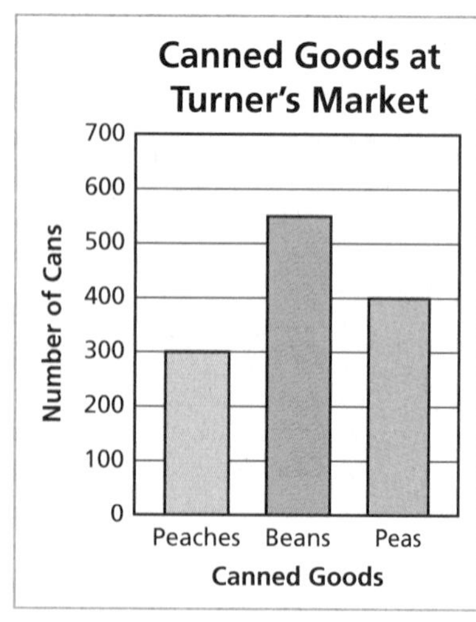

C

capacity

The amount a container can hold.

Celsius (°C)

A scale used to measure temperature.

Examples:

Water freezes at 0°C.

Water boils at 100°C.

centimeter (cm)

A metric unit used to measure length.

100 centimeters = 1 meter

column

A part of a table or array that contains items arranged vertically.

Commutative Property of Addition (Order Property of Addition)

The property that states that changing the order of addends does not change the sum.

Example:

$3 + 7 = 7 + 3$

$10 = 10$

Commutative Property of Multiplication (Order Property of Multiplication)

The property that states that changing the order of factors does not change the product.

Example:

$5 \times 4 = 4 \times 5$

$20 = 20$

comparison bars*

Bars that represent the greater amount, lesser amount, and difference in a comparison problem.

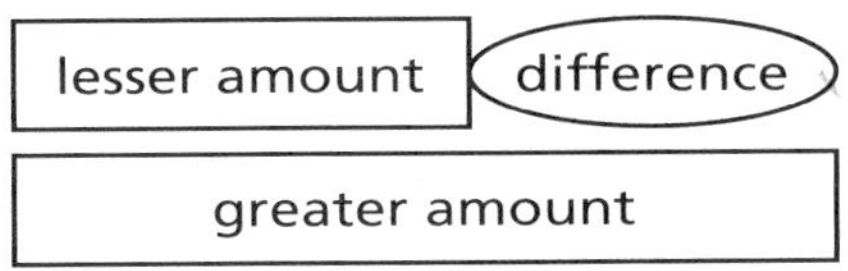

compatible numbers

Numbers that are easy to compute mentally. Compatible numbers can be used to check if answers are reasonable.

Example:

692 + 234

Some compatible numbers for the addends are 700 and 200 or 700 and 234.

concave

A polygon for which you can connect two points inside the polygon with a segment that passes outside the polygon.

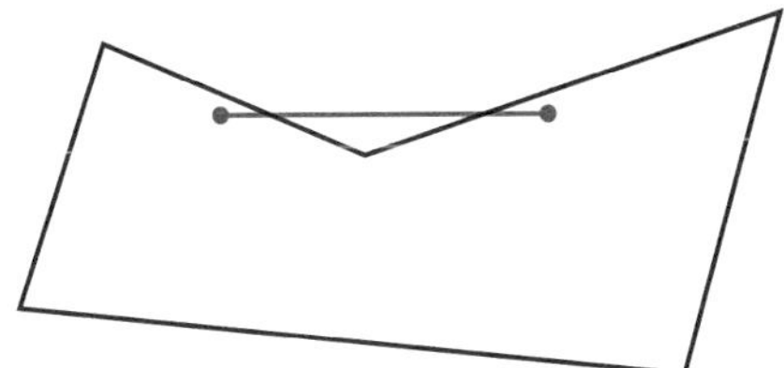

convex

A polygon is convex if all of its diagonals are inside it.

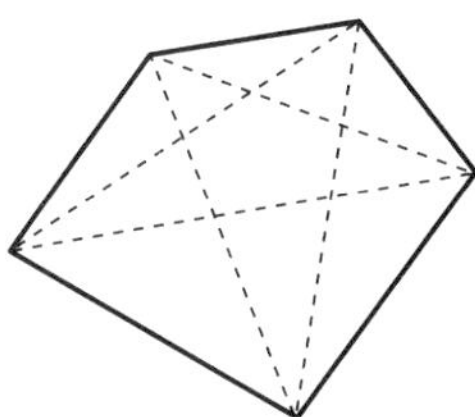

cup (c)

A U.S. customary unit of measure used to measure capacity.

1 cup = 8 fluid ounces

2 cups = 1 pint

4 cups = 1 quart

16 cups = 1 gallon

D

data

A collection of information about people or things.

decagon

A polygon with 10 sides.

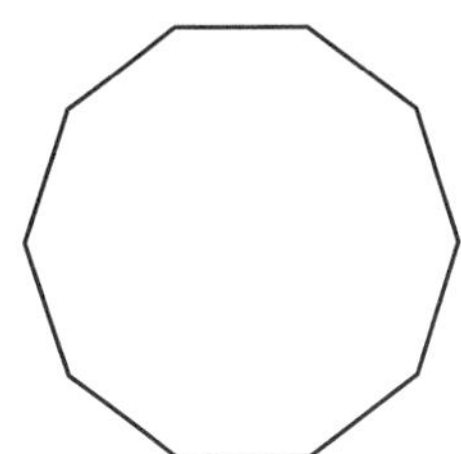

decimeter (dm)

A metric unit used to measure length.

1 decimeter = 10 centimeters

decompose

To separate or break apart (a geometric figure or a number) into smaller parts.

denominator

The bottom number in a fraction that shows the total number of equal parts in the whole.

Example:

$\frac{1}{3}$ ← denominator

diagonal

A line segment that connects two corners of a figure and is not a side of the figure.

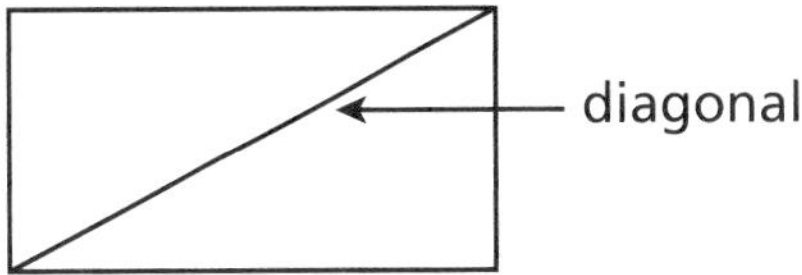

difference

The result of subtraction or of comparing.

*A classroom research-based term developed for *Math Expressions*

digit
Any of the symbols 0, 1, 2, 3, 4, 5, 6, 7, 8, 9.

digital clock
A clock that displays the hour and minutes with numbers.

Distributive Property
You can multiply a sum by a number, or multiply each addend by the number and add the products; the result is the same.

Example:

$3 \times (2 + 4) = (3 \times 2) + (3 \times 4)$

$3 \times 6 \quad = \quad 6 \quad + \quad 12$

$18 \quad = \quad 18$

dividend
The number that is divided in division.

Examples: $12 \div 3 = 4$ $\quad 3\overline{)12}$ (quotient 4)

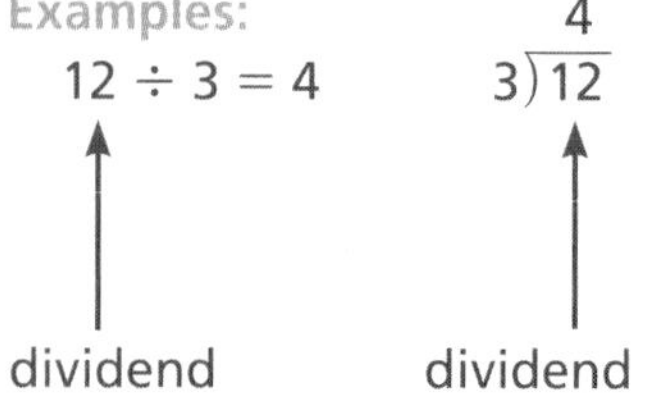

division
The mathematical operation that separates an amount into smaller equal groups to find the number of groups or the number in each group.

Example:
$12 \div 3 = 4$ is a division number sentence.

divisor
The number that you divide by in division.

Example: $12 \div 3 = 4$ $\quad 3\overline{)12}$ (quotient 4)

divisor divisor

E

elapsed time
The time that passes between the beginning and the end of an activity.

endpoint
The point at either end of a line segment or the beginning point of a ray.

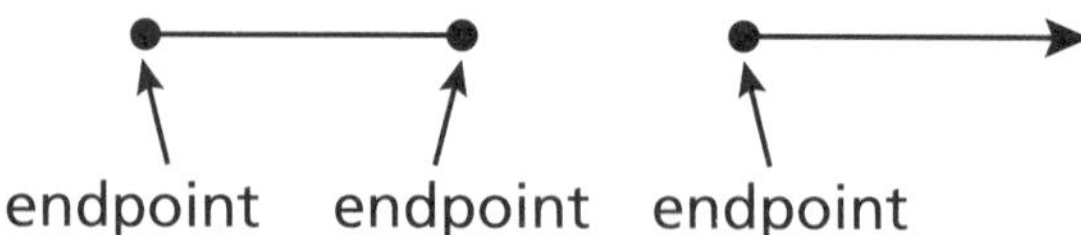

equal (=)
A symbol used to compare two amounts or values. It shows that what is on the left of the sign is equal to or the same value as what is on the right of the sign.

Example:
3,756 = 3,756

3,756 *is equal to* 3,756.

equal groups
Two or more groups with the same number of items in each group.

equation
A mathematical sentence with an equals sign.

Examples:

$11 + 22 = 33$

$75 - 25 = 50$

equivalent
Equal, or naming the same amount.

equivalent fractions
Fractions that name the same amount.

Example:

$\frac{1}{2}$ and $\frac{2}{4}$

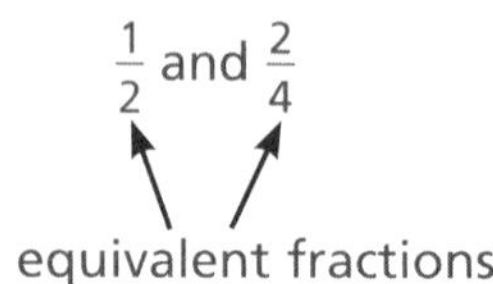

estimate
A reasonable guess about how many or about how much.

even number
A whole number that is a multiple of 2. The ones digit in an even number is 0, 2, 4, 6, or 8.

expanded form
A number written to show the value of each of its digits.

Examples:
$347 = 300 + 40 + 7$
$347 = 3$ hundreds + 4 tens + 7 ones

expression
A combination of numbers, variables, and/or operation signs. An expression does not have an equal sign.

Examples:
$4 + 7$ $a - 3$

F

factor
Any of the numbers that are multiplied to give a product.

Example:
$4 \times 5 = 20$
factor factor product

Fahrenheit (°F)
A scale used to measure temperature.

Examples:
Water freezes at 32°F.
Water boils at 212°F.

fluid ounce (fl oz)
A unit of liquid volume in the U.S. customary system that equals $\frac{1}{8}$ cup or 2 tablespoons.

foot (ft)
A U.S. customary unit used to measure length.

1 foot = 12 inches

fraction
A number that names part of a whole or part of a set.

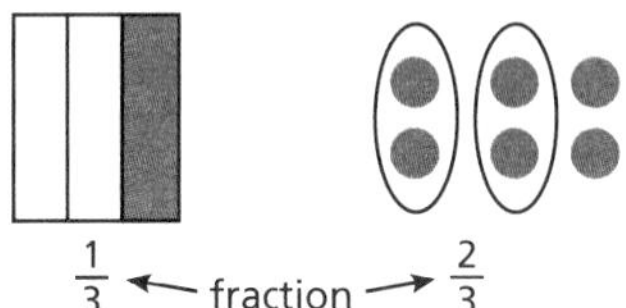

frequency table
A table that shows how many times each event, item, or category occurs.

Frequency Table	
Age	Number of Players
7	1
8	3
9	5
10	4
11	2

function table
A table of ordered pairs that shows a function.

For every input number, there is only one possible output number.

Rule: Add 2	
Input	Output
1	3
2	4
3	5
4	6

G

gallon (gal)
A U.S. customary unit used to measure capacity.

1 gallon = 4 quarts = 8 pints = 16 cups

gram (g)
A metric unit of mass. One paper clip has a mass of about 1 gram.

1,000 grams = 1 kilogram

greatest
56 29 64

64 is the greatest number.

group
To combine numbers to form new tens, hundreds, thousands, and so on.

H

height
A vertical distance, or how tall something is.

hexagon
A polygon with six sides.

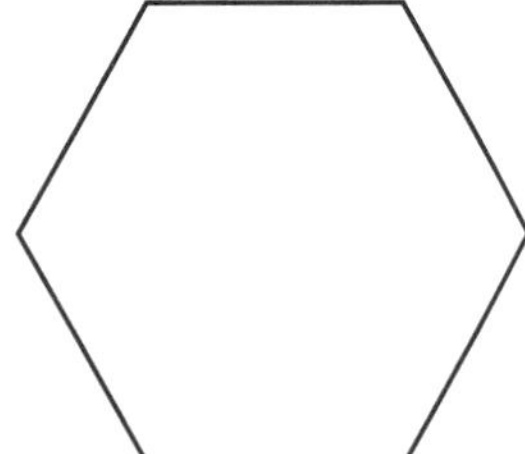

horizontal
Extending in two directions, left and right.

horizontal bar graph
A bar graph with horizontal bars.

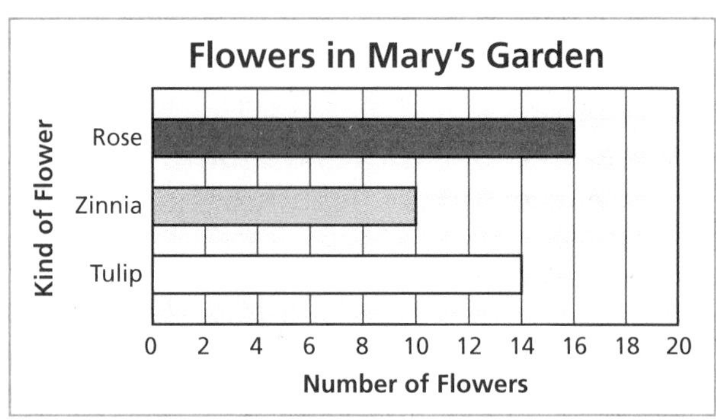

hundred thousands

Hundred Thousands	Ten Thousands	Thousands	Hundreds	Tens	Ones
5	4	6	7	8	2

There are 5 hundred thousands in 546,782.

hundreds

3 hundreds

347 has 3 hundreds.

hundreds

I

Identity Property of Addition
If 0 is added to a number, the sum equals that number.

Example:
$3 + 0 = 3$

Identity Property of Multiplication
The product of 1 and any number equals that number.

Example:
$10 \times 1 = 10$

improper fraction
A fraction in which the numerator is equal to or is greater than the denominator. Improper fractions are equal to or greater than 1.

$\frac{5}{5}$ and $\frac{8}{3}$ are improper fractions.

inch (in.)
A U.S. customary unit used to measure length.

12 inches = 1 foot

input-output table
A table that displays ordered pairs of numbers that follow a specific rule.

Rule: Add 4	
Input	**Output**
3	7
5	9
9	13
11	15
15	19

is greater than (>)
A symbol used to compare two numbers.

Example:

$6 > 5$

6 *is greater than* 5.

is less than (<)
A symbol used to compare two numbers.

Example:

$5 < 6$

5 *is less than* 6.

K

key
A part of a map, graph, or chart that explains what symbols mean.

kilogram (kg)
A metric unit of mass.

1 kilogram = 1,000 grams

kilometer (km)
A metric unit of length.

1 kilometer = 1,000 meters

L

least
72 41 89

41 is the least number.

line
A straight path that goes on forever in opposite directions.

line plot
A diagram that shows frequency of data on a number line. Also called a *dot plot*.

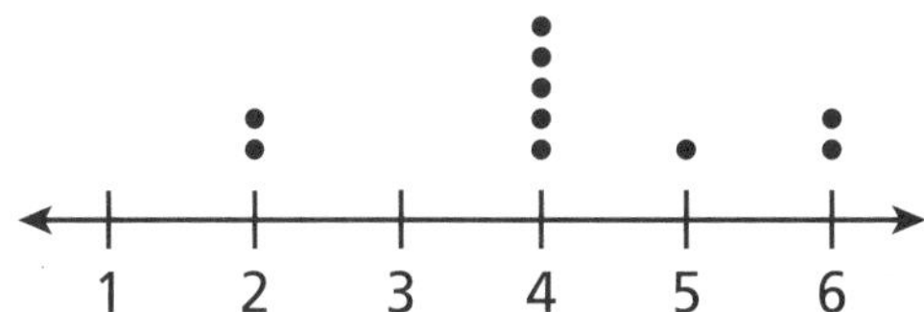

line segment
A part of a line. A line segment has two endpoints.

liquid volume
A measure of how much a container can hold. Also called *capacity*.

liter (L)
A metric unit used to measure capacity.

1 liter = 1,000 milliliters

Glossary

M

mass
The amount of matter in an object.

mental math
A way to solve problems without using pencil and paper or a calculator.

meter (m)
A metric unit used to measure length.
1 meter = 100 centimeters

method
A procedure, or way, of doing something.

mile (mi)
A U.S. customary unit of length.
1 mile = 5,280 feet

milliliter (mL)
A metric unit used to measure capacity.
1,000 milliliters = 1 liter

mixed number
A whole number and a fraction.
$1\frac{3}{4}$ is a mixed number.

multiple
A number that is the product of the given number and any whole number.

multiplication
A mathematical operation that combines equal groups.

Example:

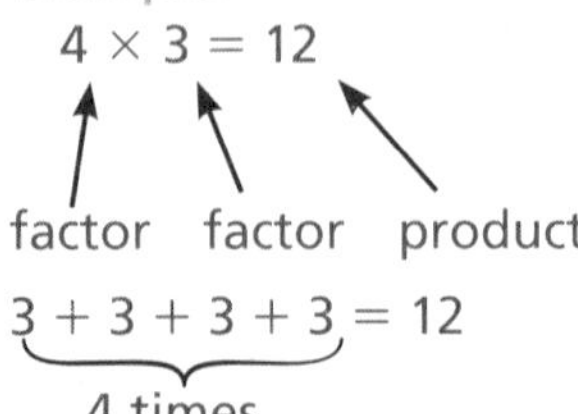

N

number line
A line on which numbers are assigned to lengths.

numerator
The top number in a fraction that shows the number of equal parts counted.

Example:

$\frac{1}{3}$ ← numerator

O

octagon
A polygon with eight sides.

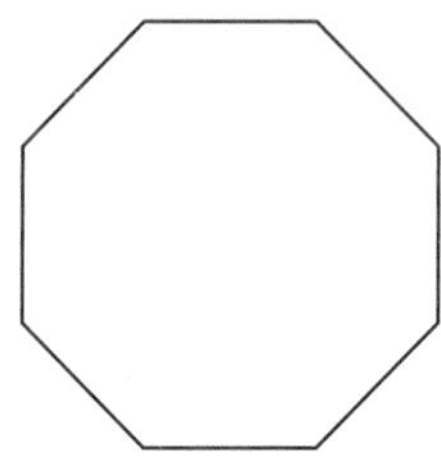

odd number
A whole number that is not a multiple of 2. The ones digit in an odd number is 1, 3, 5, 7, or 9.

ones

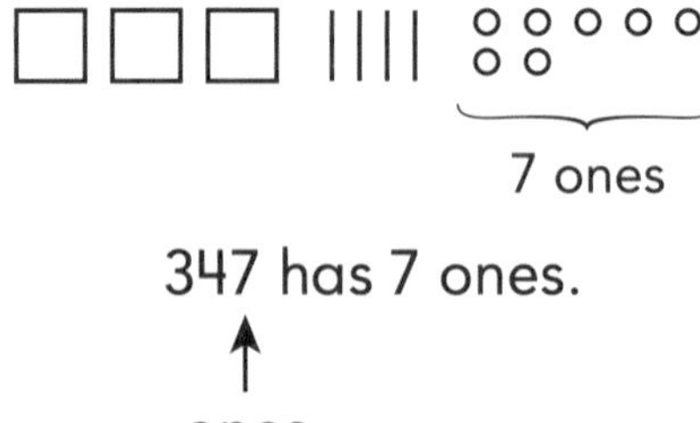

347 has 7 ones.
↑
ones

opposite sides
Sides of a polygon that are across from each other; they do not meet at a point.

Example:

Sides *a* and *c* are opposite.

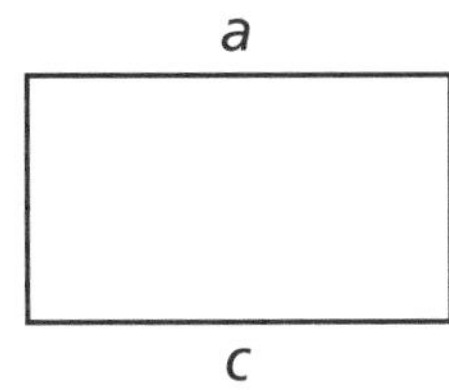

Order of Operations
A set of rules that state the order in which the operations in an expression should be done.

STEP 1: Perform operations inside parentheses first.

STEP 2: Multiply and divide from left to right.

STEP 3: Add and subtract from left to right.

ounce (oz)
A U.S. customary unit used to measure weight.

16 ounces = 1 pound

P

parallel
Two lines are parallel if they never cross or meet. They are the same distance apart.

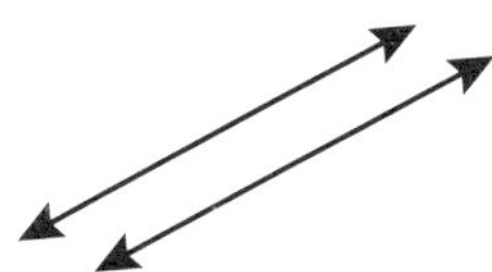

parallelogram
A quadrilateral with both pairs of opposite sides parallel.

pentagon
A polygon with five sides.

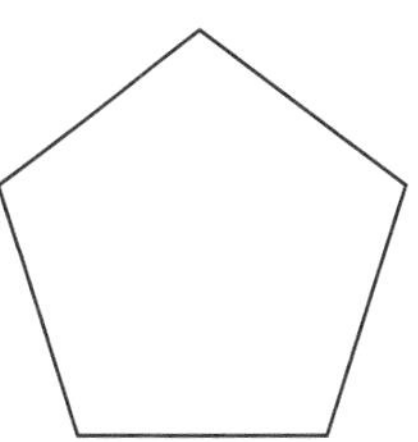

perimeter
The distance around a figure.

Example:

Perimeter = 3 cm + 5 cm + 3 cm + 5 cm = 16 cm

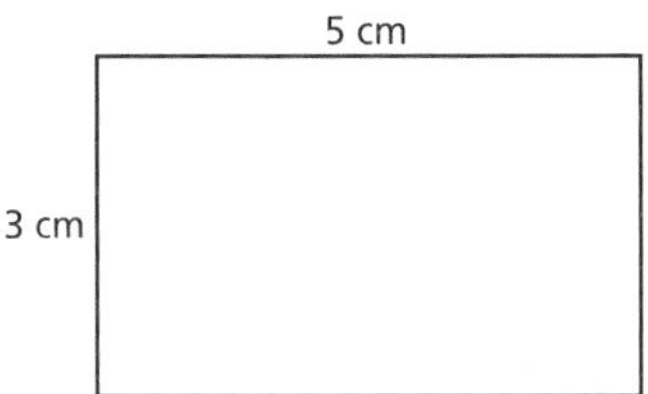

perpendicular
Two lines are perpendicular if they cross or meet to form square corners.

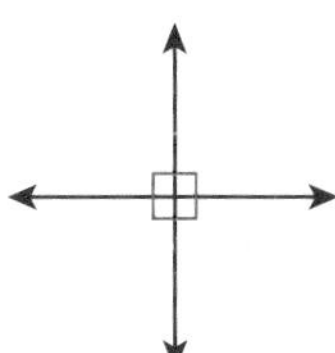

pictograph
A graph that uses pictures or symbols to represent data.

Favorite Ice Cream Flavors

Peanut Butter Crunch	
Cherry Vanilla	
Chocolate	

Each stands for 4 votes.

pint (pt)
A U.S. customary unit used to measure capacity.

1 pint = 2 cups

place value

The value assigned to the place that a digit occupies in a number.

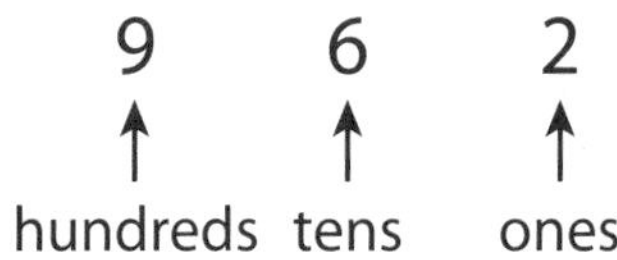

place value drawing

A drawing that represents a number. Hundreds are represented by boxes, tens by vertical lines, and ones by small circles.

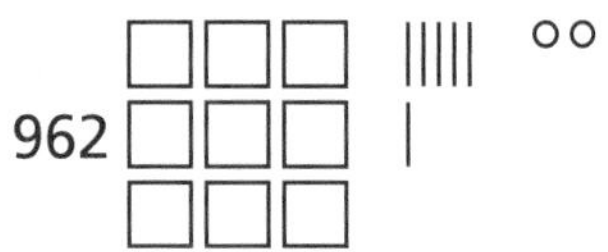

P.M.

The time period between noon and midnight.

polygon

A closed plane figure with sides made up of straight line segments.

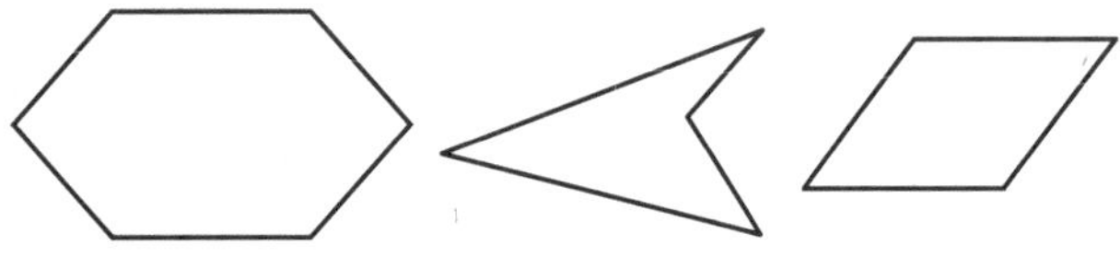

pound (lb)

A U.S. customary unit used to measure weight.

1 pound = 16 ounces

product

The answer when you multiply numbers.

Example:

$4 \times 7 = 28$

factor factor product

proof drawing*

A drawing used to show that an answer is correct.

249
+ 386
11
635

Q

quadrilateral

A polygon with four sides.

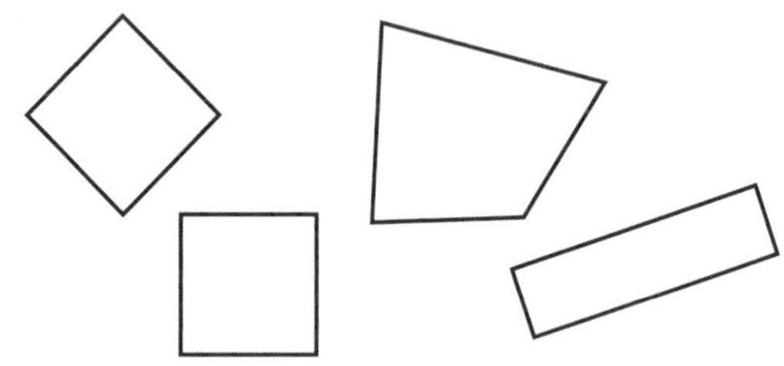

quart (qt)

A U.S. customary unit used to measure capacity.

1 quart = 4 cups

quotient

The answer when you divide numbers.

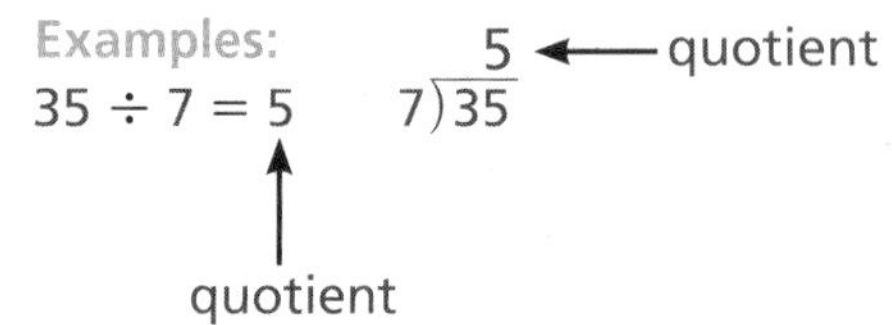

R

ray

A part of a line that has one endpoint and goes on forever in one direction.

*A classroom research-based term developed for *Math Expressions*

rectangle
A parallelogram that has four right angles.

rhombus
A parallelogram with equal sides.

right angle
An angle that measures 90°.

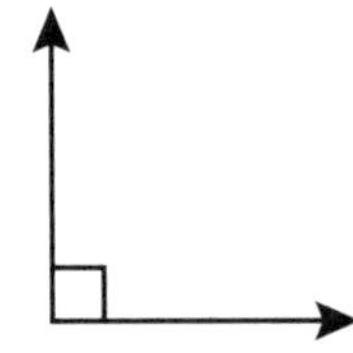

round
To find about how many or how much by expressing a number to the nearest ten, hundred, thousand, and so on.

row
A part of a table or array that contains items arranged horizontally.

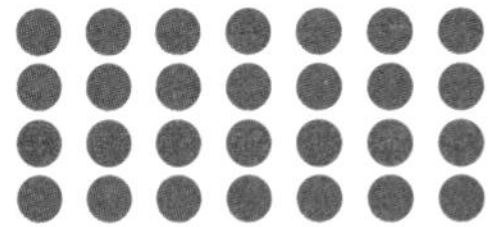

rule
For an input-output table, a *rule* is applied to the input to find the output.

Rule: Add 4	
Input	**Output**
3	7
5	9
9	13
11	15
15	19

S

scale
An arrangement of numbers in order with equal intervals.

side (of a figure)
One of the line segments that make up a polygon.

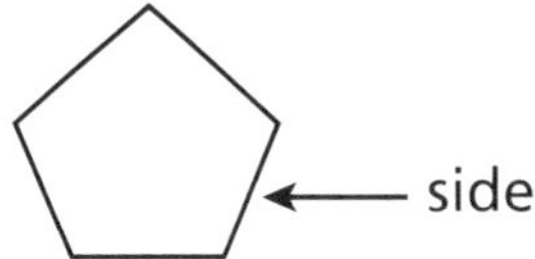

simplify
To write an equivalent fraction with a smaller numerator and denominator.

situation equation*
An equation that shows the action or the relationship in a problem.

Example:
$35 + n = 40$

solution equation*
An equation that shows the operation to perform in order to solve the problem.

Example:
$n = 40 - 35$

square
A rectangle with four sides of the same length.

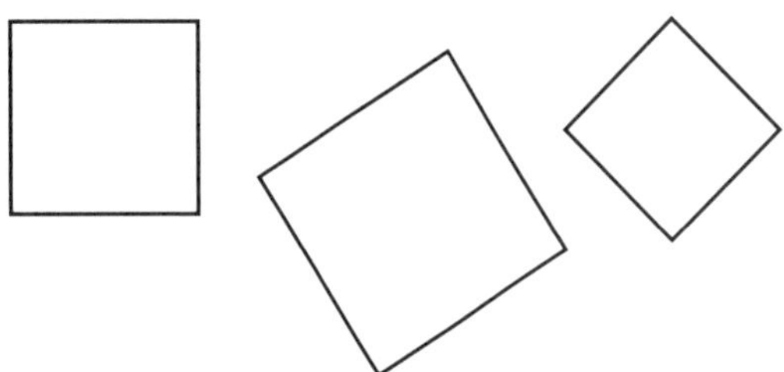

*A classroom research-based term developed for *Math Expressions*

square number
The product of a whole number and itself.

Example:
$4 \times 4 = 16$

square number

square unit
A unit of area equal to the area of a square with one-unit sides.

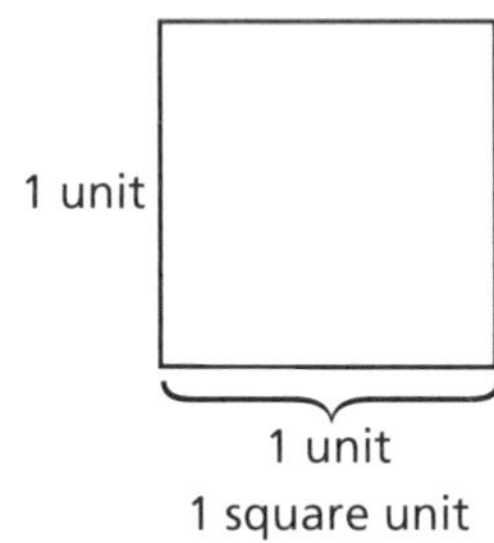

standard form
The name of a number written using digits.

Example:
1,829

subtract
To find the difference of two numbers.

Example:
$18 - 11 = 7$

subtraction
A mathematical operation on two numbers that gives the difference.

Example:
$43 - 40 = 3$

sum
The answer when adding two or more addends.

Example:
$37 + 52 = 89$

addend addend sum

T

table
An easy-to-read arrangement of data, usually in rows and columns.

Favorite Team Sport	
Sport	**Number of Students**
Baseball	35
Soccer	60
Basketball	40

tally chart
A chart used to record and organize data with tally marks.

Tally Chart	
Age	**Tally**
7	|
8	|||
9	卌

tally marks
Short line segments drawn in groups of 5. Each mark, including the slanted mark, stands for 1 unit.

卌 卌 ||| means 13
5 5 3

temperature
The measure of how hot or cold something is.

ten thousands

Hundred Thousands	Ten Thousands	Thousands	Hundreds	Tens	Ones
5	4	6	7	8	2

There are 4 ten thousands in 546,782.

tens

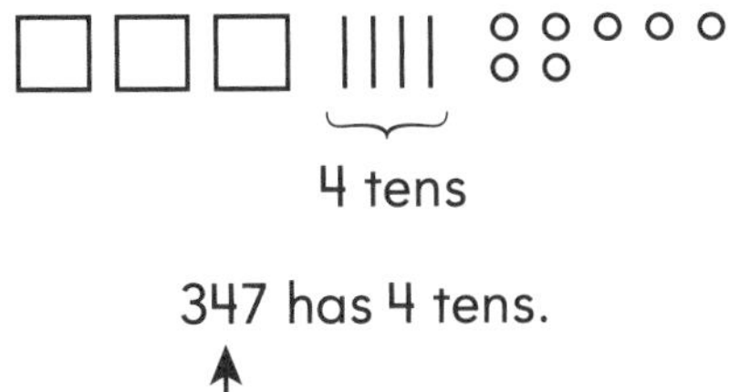

thermometer
A tool that is used to measure temperature.

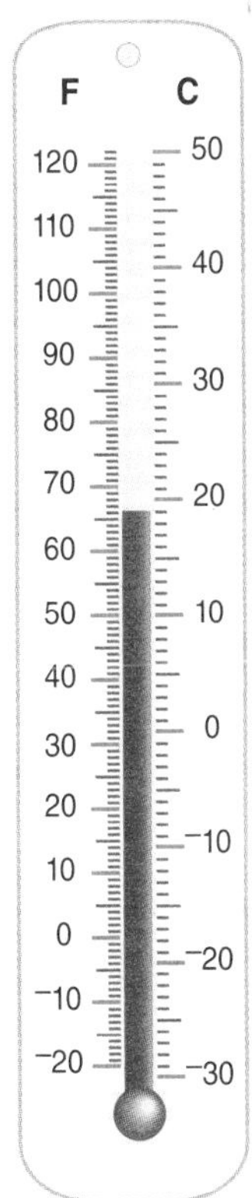

thousands

Hundred Thousands	Ten Thousands	Thousands	Hundreds	Tens	Ones
5	4	6	7	8	2

There are 6 thousands in 546,782.

total
The answer when adding two or more addends. The sum of two or more numbers.

Example:

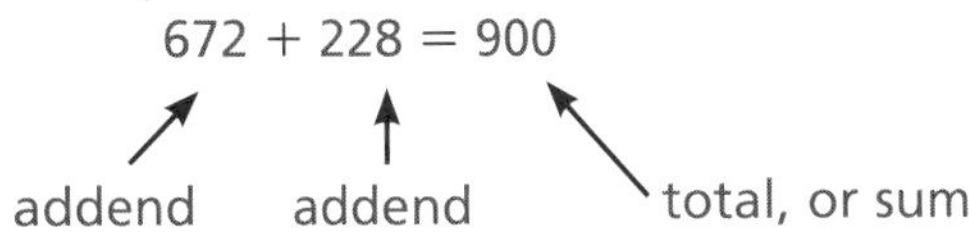

trapezoid
A quadrilateral with exactly one pair of parallel sides.

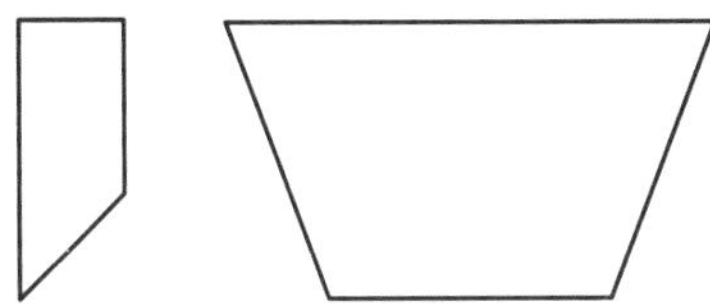

triangle
A polygon with three sides.

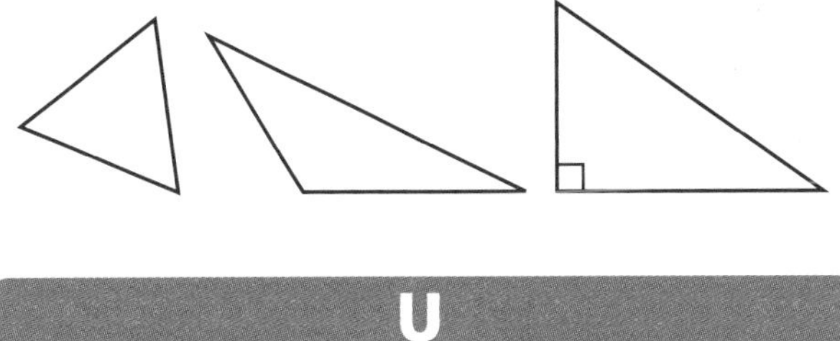

U

ungroup*
To open up 1 in a given place to make 10 of the next smaller place value in order to subtract.

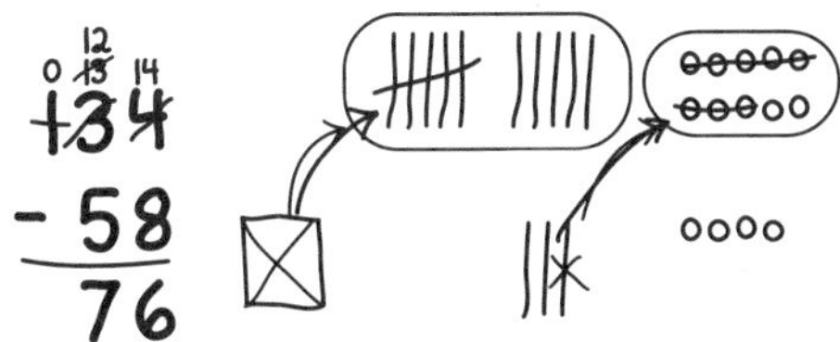

unit fraction
A fraction whose numerator is 1. It shows one equal part of a whole.

Example:

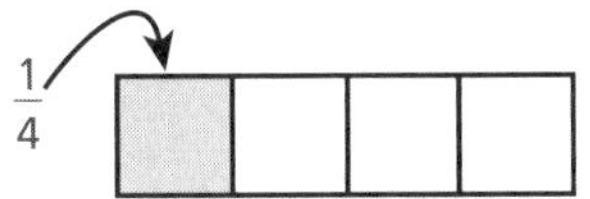

*A classroom research-based term developed for *Math Expressions*

unit square
A square whose area is 1 square unit.

V

variable
A letter or symbol used to represent an unknown number in an algebraic expression or equation.

Example:
$2 + n$
n is a variable.

Venn diagram
A diagram that uses circles to show the relationship among sets of objects.

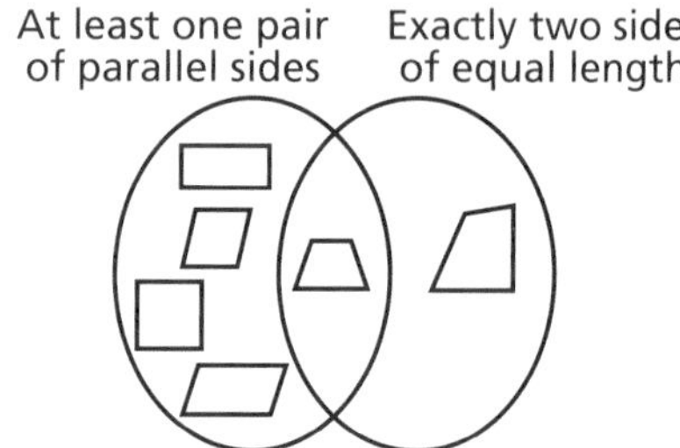

vertex
A point where sides, rays, or edges meet.

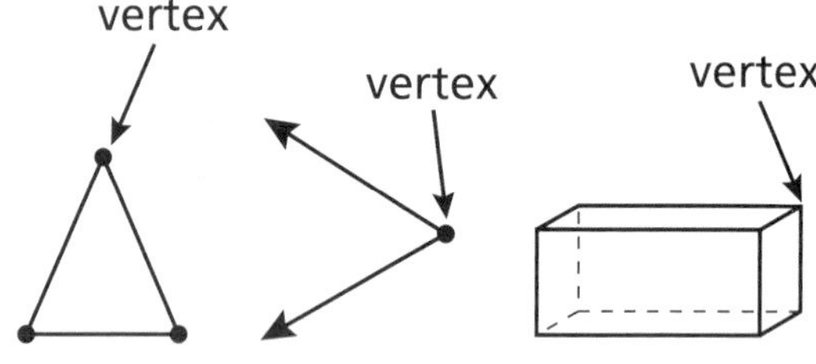

vertical
Extending in two directions, up and down.

vertical bar graph
A bar graph with vertical bars.

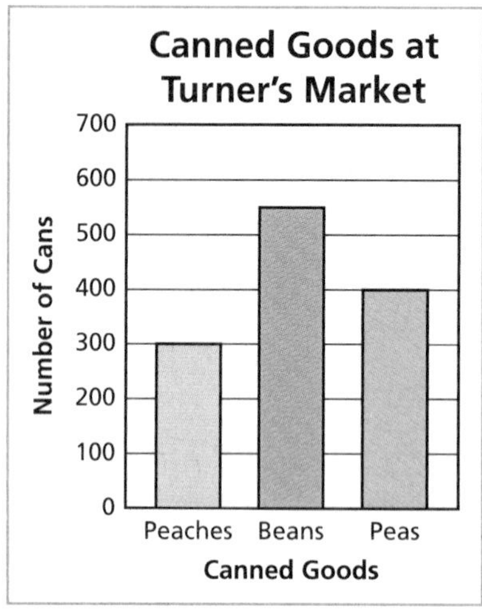

W

weight
The measure of how heavy something is.

word form
A name of a number written using words instead of digits.

Example:
Nine hundred eighty-four

Y

yard (yd)
A U.S. customary unit used to measure length.

1 yard = 3 feet = 36 inches

Z

Zero Property of Multiplication
If 0 is multiplied by a number, the product is 0.

Example:
$3 \times 0 = 0$

3.ARO Algebraic Reasoning and Operations

3.ARO.1	Given an expression such as 3 × 8, describe the product as the total number of objects in 3 groups of 8 objects.	Unit 1 Lessons 1, 2, 3, 4, 5, 6, 7, 8, 9, 10, 12, 13, 14, 16, 18, 19; Unit 2 Lessons 2, 4, 7, 9, 10, 11, 13, 15
3.ARO.2	Given an expression such as 35 ÷ 7, describe the quotient as the *number of objects in a group* when 35 objects are separated into equal shares, or the *number of equal shares* when 35 objects are separated into equal groups of 7 objects.	Unit 1 Lessons 4, 5, 6, 7, 9, 10, 12, 13, 14, 16, 17, 18, 19; Unit 2 Lessons 2, 4, 7, 9, 10, 11, 13, 15
3.ARO.3	Solve multiplication and division word problems through 100 involving arrays, equal groups, and measurements (example: area model); represent the problem using for example, pictures and equations that have symbols for the unknown quantity.	Unit 1 Lessons 2, 3, 4, 5, 6, 7, 9, 10, 12, 13, 14, 16, 17, 18, 19; Unit 2 Lessons 2, 4, 7, 9, 10, 11, 13, 15; Unit 3 Lessons 20, 21; Unit 4 Lesson 15; Unit 5 Lesson 5; Unit 6 Lessons 2, 3, 8, 9, 10, 11; Unit 7 Lessons 1, 2, 3, 4
3.ARO.4	Given a multiplication or division equation involving 3 whole numbers, find the unknown quantity that makes the equation true.	Unit 1 Lessons 1, 4, 5, 6, 7, 8, 9, 10, 12, 13, 14, 16, 17, 18, 19; Unit 2 Lessons 1, 2, 3, 4, 5, 6, 7, 8, 9, 10, 11, 13, 14, 15; Unit 5 Lesson 2; Unit 6 Lessons 2, 3
3.ARO.5	Use properties of operations as strategies for multiplying and dividing.	Unit 1 Lessons 3, 6, 11, 12, 14, 15, 19; Unit 2 Lessons 1, 8, 12, 15; Unit 5 Lesson 2
3.ARO.6	Use multiplication knowledge to recognize that division can be thought of as an unknown factor problem.	Unit 1 Lessons 4, 5, 6, 7, 8, 9, 10, 11, 12, 13, 14, 15, 16, 17, 18; Unit 2 Lessons 1, 2, 3, 4, 5, 6, 7, 8, 9, 10, 11, 12, 13, 14; Unit 5 Lesson 2
3.ARO.7	Demonstrate fluency in multiplying and dividing through 100 by using strategies like the properties of operations or the relationship between multiplication and division (example: if you know 4 × 7 = 28 then you know 28 ÷ 4 = 7). Know the products of two 1-digit numbers from memory by the end of Grade 3.	Unit 1 Lessons 1, 2, 3, 4, 5, 6, 7, 8, 9, 10, 11, 12, 13, 14, 15, 16, 17, 18, 19; Unit 2 Lessons 1, 2, 3, 4, 5, 6, 7, 8, 9, 10, 11, 12, 13, 14, 15

3.ARO.8	Use the four operations to solve two-step word problems; represent the problems with equations using a letter for an unknown quantity. Determine if an answer is reasonable by estimating (example: round to estimate the answer) and using mental math.	Unit 2 Lessons 9, 10, 11, 13; Unit 3 Lessons 17, 19; Unit 6 Lessons 7, 8, 9, 10, 11
3.ARO.9	Find arithmetic patterns (example: find patterns in addition and multiplication tables). Use properties of operations to explain the patterns.	Unit 1 Lessons 1, 5, 6, 7, 8, 10, 12, 15, 19; Unit 2 Lessons 1, 3, 5, 6, 8, 14, 15; Unit 3 Lesson 17
3.ARO.10	Create, describe, and apply single-operation input-output rules involving addition, subtraction and multiplication to solve problems in various contexts.	Unit 3 Lesson 22

3.PVO Place Value and Operations

3.PVO.1	Understand how to use place value when rounding whole numbers to the nearest 10, 100, 1,000, and 10,000.	Unit 3 Lessons 1, 2, 3, 4, 5, 6, 10, 18, 19; Unit 6 Lessons 4, 8
3.PVO.2	Use strategies and algorithms reflecting properties of operations, place value, and/or the fact that addition and subtraction are related, to fluently add and subtract through 1,000.	Unit 3 Lessons 2, 3, 4, 5, 6, 7, 8, 9, 10, 11, 12, 13, 14, 15, 16, 18; Unit 4 Lessons 12, 13; Unit 6 Lessons 1, 2, 3, 4, 5, 6, 8, 9, 10, 11; Unit 7 Lessons 1, 2, 3
3.PVO.3	Use place value and properties of operations to multiply a 1-digit number and a multiple of 10 through 90 (example: 6×40 and 9×70).	Unit 2 Lesson 12; Unit 3 Lessons 20, 21
3.PVO.4	Read, write and demonstrate multiple equivalent representations for numbers up to 100,000 using objects, visual representations, including standard form, word form, expanded form, and expanded notation.	Unit 3 Lesson 19
3.PVO.5	Compare whole numbers through the hundred thousands and represent the comparisons using the symbols $>$, $<$, or $=$.	Unit 3 Lesson 19
3.PVO.6	Find 10,000 more or 10,000 less than a given five-digit number. Find 1,000 more or 1,000 less than a given four- or five-digit. Find 100 more or 100 less than a given four- or five-digit number.	Unit 3 Lesson 19
3.PVO.7	Use strategies and algorithms based on knowledge of place value, equality and properties of addition and multiplication to multiply a two- or three-digit number by a one-digit number.	Unit 3 Lessons 20, 21

3.FO Fractions and Operations		
3.FO.1	Understand that a unit fraction, $\frac{1}{b}$, represents one part of a whole that has been separated into b equal parts (example: $\frac{1}{3}$ is one of 3 equal parts) and the fraction $\frac{a}{b}$ is formed by $\frac{1}{b}$-size parts (example: $\frac{2}{3}$ can be thought of as putting together two $\frac{1}{3}$ parts). Find parts of a set using visual representations.	Unit 4 Lessons 1, 2, 4, 5; Unit 5 Lessons 9, 10
3.FO.2	Recognize that fractions can be indicated on a number line. Use a number line to represent fractions.	Unit 4 Lessons 2, 3, 4
3.FO.2.a	Use a number line to show a unit fraction $\frac{1}{b}$. Know that the interval from 0 to 1 represents the whole; to show $\frac{1}{b}$ the whole must be separated into b equal parts. Understand that from 0 to the first endpoint of the partitioned whole is where the fraction $\frac{1}{b}$ is located.	Unit 4 Lessons 2, 3; Unit 5 Lesson 8
3.FO.2.b	Draw a number line to locate fractions; starting at 0 and ending at 1, separate the whole into a equal-size parts, $\frac{1}{b}$. Understand that the length of the interval created is $\frac{a}{b}$, and the endpoint of the interval locates $\frac{a}{b}$.	Unit 4 Lessons 2, 3, 4; Unit 5 Lesson 8
3.FO.3	Understand special cases of equivalent fractions and explain why such fractions are equivalent. Reason about size to compare and order fractions.	Unit 4 Lessons 2, 3, 4, 5; Unit 5 Lessons 7, 9, 10
3.FO.3.a	Given two fractions, understand that they are equivalent if their size is the same, or if they are located at the same point on the number line.	Unit 4 Lesson 3; Unit 5 Lessons 8, 9
3.FO.3.b	Recognize and find equivalent fractions less than 1 (example: $\frac{1}{3} = \frac{3}{6}$ and $\frac{1}{4} = \frac{2}{8}$). Use methods such as, making models, to explain why the fractions are equivalent.	Unit 5 Lessons 7, 8, 9, 10
3.FO.3.c	Write a whole number as a fraction; identify fractions equivalent to whole numbers.	Unit 4 Lessons 2, 3; Unit 5 Lessons 8, 9
3.FO.3.d	Use reasoning about size to compare and order fractions with the same numerator but different denominators, or with the same denominator. Understand that to make an accurate comparison, the two fractions must refer to the same whole. Record the comparison with symbols $>$, $<$, or $=$, and justify the results (example: use a picture or other model).	Unit 4 Lessons 4, 5; Unit 5 Lessons 9, 10
3.FO.4	Explain and demonstrate how fractions $\frac{1}{4}$, $\frac{1}{2}$, $\frac{3}{4}$ and a whole relate to time, measurement, and money, and demonstrate using visual representation.	Unit 4 Lesson 11; Unit 5 Lesson 9

3.MDA Measurement and Data Analysis		
3.MDA.1	Know how to tell and write time to the nearest minute and measure time in minutes. Use a number line, or other methods, to solve word problems that involve adding and subtracting time in minutes. Know relationships among units of time.	Unit 4 Lessons 7, 8, 9, 10, 11
3.MDA.2	Use the standard units, liter (L), grams (g), and kilograms (kg) to measure and estimate liquid volume and mass. Solve one-step problems about mass or volume given in the same units and that involve the four operations. Represent the problem by using a diagram (example: a number line) or other methods.	Unit 7 Lessons 1, 2, 3, 4
3.MDA.2.a	Solve problems and make change involving money using a combination of coins and bills.	Unit 5 Lessons 11, 12
3.MDA.2.b	Solve problems involving estimating of temperature and use an analog thermometer to determine temperature to the nearest degree in Fahrenheit and Celsius.	Unit 4 Lesson 14; Unit 5 Lessons 11, 12
3.MDA.3	Given a collection of data in several categories, make a picture graph and bar graph with labeled scales. Use information from bar graphs to solve one- and two-step problems to answer *how many more* and *how many less* questions. Collect data through observations, surveys, and experiments.	Unit 4 Lessons 12, 13, 14, 15
3.MDA.4	Create a group of data by estimating and measuring lengths with customary units (inch, half-inch, quarter-inch) or the metric unit, centimeter. Use a line plot to display the data, labeling the horizontal scale with the correct units (example: whole inches, half-inches, or quarter-inches).	Unit 4 Lessons 6, 14, 15, 16
3.MDA.5	Know that area is an attribute of two-dimensional (plane) figures; understand concepts of area measurement.	Unit 1 Lesson 11; Unit 2 Lesson 2; Unit 4 Lesson 6; Unit 5 Lessons 1, 3, 5, 6
3.MDA.5.a	Recognize that a *unit square* has a side length of *1 unit* and an area of *1 square unit* and can be used to measure area of plane figures.	Unit 1 Lesson 11; Unit 2 Lesson 2; Unit 5 Lessons 1, 3
3.MDA.5.b	Understand that if a plane figure can be covered by *n* unit squares without having gaps or overlaps, then the figure has an area of *n* square units.	Unit 1 Lesson 11; Unit 2 Lesson 2; Unit 5 Lessons 1, 3, 6
3.MDA.6	Count unit squares to find the area of a figure; use standard units (square inch, square foot, square centimeter, square meter) and non-standard units (example: tiles) to measure area.	Unit 1 Lesson 11; Unit 5 Lessons 1, 2, 4, 6

3.MDA.7	Understand the relationship between area and the operations of multiplication and addition.	Unit 1 Lessons 11, 12; Unit 2 Lesson 1; Unit 3 Lessons 20, 21; Unit 5 Lessons 1, 2, 3; Unit Lesson 9
3.MDA.7.a	Use tiling to find the area of rectangles with given side lengths; show that the resulting area can also be found by multiplying the two side lengths.	Unit 1 Lesson 11; Unit 2 Lesson 2; Unit 5 Lessons 1, 2
3.MDA.7.b	Solve real-world and other mathematical problems that involve finding the area of rectangles by multiplying the side lengths (given in whole-numbers); use reasoning to illustrate the products as rectangular areas.	Unit 1 Lessons 11,12; Unit 2 Lessons 2, 6; Unit 5 Lessons 1, 2, 3, 4, 5; Unit 7 Lesson 9
3.MDA.7.c	Use reasoning and area models to represent the Distributive Property: given a rectangle that has side lengths a and $b + c$ use tiles to illustrate understanding that the area is the sum of $a \times b$ and $a \times c$.	Unit 1 Lessons 11, 12, 14; Unit 2 Lesson 1; Unit 5 Lesson 2
3.MDA.7.d	Recognize that addition can be used to find area. Partition rectilinear figures (example: composite rectangular figures) into rectangles having no overlaps, then find the area of the original figure by adding the areas of the parts; use this approach to solve real-world problems.	Unit 1 Lessons 11, 12; Unit 5 Lessons 2, 4, 5, 6
3.MDA.8	Solve problems (real world and other mathematical contexts) that involve perimeters of polygons in the following situations: given side lengths, find perimeter; given perimeter and a side length, find the unknown length; find rectangles with the same perimeter and different areas or same area and different perimeters.	Unit 5 Lessons 1, 2, 3, 5; Unit 7 Lesson 9
3.MDA.9	Measure distances around objects.	Unit 4 Lesson 14

3.GSR Geometry and Spatial Reasoning

3.GSR.1	Recognize that geometric figures belonging to different categories may have attributes in common and these shared attributes can form a larger category (example: although squares, rectangles, and rhombuses belong to different categories they share the attributes four sides, four angles, and four vertices and belong to the larger category, quadrilaterals.) Know that squares, rectangles, and rhombuses are quadrilaterals; sketch quadrilaterals that are not in those categories.	Unit 7 Lessons 5, 6, 7, 8, 9
3.GSR.2	Separate geometric figures into parts with equal areas. Represent the area of a part as a unit fraction of the whole.	Unit 4 Lessons 1, 2, 4, 5; Unit 5 Lesson 10; Unit 7 Lesson 5
3.GSR.3	Identify parallel and perpendicular lines in various contexts, and use them to describe and create geometric figures such as right triangles, rectangles, parallelograms and trapezoids.	Unit 7 Lessons 5, 6, 7, 8

MPP1	
Problem Solving	Unit 1 Lessons 3, 4, 5, 6, 7, 9, 10, 12, 13, 14, 16, 18, 19 Unit 2 Lessons 1, 2, 4, 7, 9, 10, 13, 15 Unit 3 Lessons 3, 4, 5, 6, 7, 8, 9, 10, 11, 12, 14, 15, 16, 17, 18, 20, 21 Unit 4 Lessons 9, 10, 11, 12, 13, 14, 15, 16 Unit 5 Lessons 2, 5, 9, 10, 11 Unit 6 Lessons 1, 2, 3, 4, 5, 6, 7, 8, 9, 10, 11 Unit 7 Lessons 1, 2, 3, 4, 5, 9
MPP2	
Abstract and Quantitative Reasoning	Unit 1 Lessons 1, 3, 5, 7, 8, 10, 11, 12, 19 Unit 2 Lessons 1, 2, 3, 5, 6, 8, 13, 15 Unit 3 Lessons 1, 2, 5, 6, 8, 9, 11, 12, 13, 14, 15, 16, 17, 18, 19, 20, 22 Unit 4 Lessons 1, 2, 3, 4, 5, 6, 9, 11, 12, 16 Unit 5 Lessons 1, 2, 3, 4, 5, 7, 8, 9, 10 Unit 6 Lessons 1, 2, 3, 4, 8, 11 Unit 7 Lessons 1, 2, 3, 5, 9
MPP3	
Use and Evaluate Logical Reasoning	Unit 1 Lessons 1, 2, 3, 4, 5, 6, 7, 8, 9, 10, 11, 12, 13, 14, 15, 16, 18, 19 Unit 2 Lessons 1, 2, 3, 4, 5, 6, 8, 9, 10, 11, 12, 13, 14, 15 Unit 3 Lessons 1, 2, 3, 4, 5, 6, 7, 8, 9, 10, 11, 12, 13, 14, 15, 16, 17, 18, 20, 21, 22 Unit 4 Lessons 1, 2, 3, 4, 5, 6, 7, 8, 9, 10, 11, 12, 13, 14, 15, 16 Unit 5 Lessons 1, 2, 3, 4, 5, 7, 8, 9, 10, 11, 12 Unit 6 Lessons 1, 2, 3, 4, 5, 6, 7, 8, 9, 10, 11 Unit 7 Lessons 1, 2, 3, 4, 5, 6, 8, 9
MPP4	
Mathematical Modeling	Unit 1 Lessons 1, 2, 3, 4, 5, 6, 7, 9, 10, 12, 13, 14, 15, 16, 17, 18, 19 Unit 2 Lessons 2, 4, 7, 9, 11, 13, 15 Unit 3 Lessons 3, 4, 8, 9, 10, 11, 12, 14, 16, 17, 18, 20, 21, 22 Unit 4 Lessons 9, 10, 11, 12, 13, 14, 16 Unit 5 Lessons 2, 5, 9, 10, 11 Unit 6 Lessons 1, 2, 3, 4, 8, 9, 10, 11 Unit 7 Lessons 1, 2, 3, 4, 5, 9

MPP5	
Use Mathematical Tools	Unit 1 Lessons 1, 2, 3, 4, 5, 6, 7, 8, 9, 10, 11, 12, 13, 14, 15, 16, 17, 18 Unit 2 Lessons 1, 2, 3, 4, 5, 6, 7, 8, 9, 10, 11, 12, 13, 14, 15 Unit 3 Lessons 1, 2, 3, 4, 5, 6, 7, 8, 13, 17, 18, 19, 20, 21 Unit 4 Lessons 1, 2, 3, 5, 6, 7, 8, 9, 10, 11, 14, 16 Unit 5 Lessons 1, 2, 6, 7, 8, 11, 12 Unit 6 Lessons 4, 11 Unit 7 Lessons 2, 3, 5, 7, 8, 9
MPP6	
Use Precise Mathematical Language	Unit 1 Lessons 1, 2, 3, 4, 5, 6, 7, 8, 9, 10, 11, 12, 13, 14, 15, 16, 18, 19 Unit 2 Lessons 1, 2, 3, 4, 5, 6, 7, 8, 9, 10, 11, 12, 13, 14, 15 Unit 3 Lessons 1, 2, 3, 4, 5, 6, 7, 8, 9, 10, 11, 12, 13, 14, 15, 16, 17, 18, 19, 20, 21, 22 Unit 4 Lessons 1, 2, 3, 4, 5, 6, 7, 8, 9, 10, 11, 12, 13, 14, 15, 16 Unit 5 Lessons 1, 2, 3, 4, 5, 7, 8, 9, 11 Unit 6 Lessons 1, 2, 3, 4, 5, 6, 7, 8, 9, 10, 11 Unit 7 Lessons 1, 2, 3, 4, 5, 6, 7, 8, 9
MPP7	
See Structure	Unit 1 Lessons 1, 2, 4, 5, 6, 7, 8, 10, 11, 12, 13, 15, 17, 18, 19 Unit 2 Lessons 1, 3, 5, 6, 14, 15 Unit 3 Lessons 1, 2, 3, 4, 11, 14, 16, 17, 18, 19, 21, 22 Unit 4 Lessons 1, 2, 3, 13, 16 Unit 5 Lessons 1, 4, 6, 7, 10 Unit 6 Lessons 1, 2, 3, 5, 8, 11 Unit 7 Lessons 1, 5, 6, 7, 8, 9
MPP8	
Generalize	Unit 1 Lessons 1, 3, 5, 7, 8, 10, 11, 13, 15, 19 Unit 2 Lessons 1, 3, 5, 6, 10, 12, 14, 15 Unit 3 Lessons 5, 6, 14, 17, 18, 19, 20 Unit 4 Lessons 1, 2, 3, 4, 5, 6, 15, 16 Unit 5 Lessons 3, 6, 7, 8, 9, 10, 11 Unit 6 Lessons 1, 2, 4, 11 Unit 7 Lessons 3, 5, 8, 9

A

B

C

D

E

F

G

N

O

P

Q

R

V

W

Z

Number Tables

Multiplication Table and Scrambled Tables (Volume 1)

A

×	1	2	3	4	5	6	7	8	9	10
1	1	2	3	4	5	6	7	8	9	10
2	2	4	6	8	10	12	14	16	18	20
3	3	6	9	12	15	18	21	24	27	30
4	4	8	12	16	20	24	28	32	36	40
5	5	10	15	20	25	30	35	40	45	50
6	6	12	18	24	30	36	42	48	54	60
7	7	14	21	28	35	42	49	56	63	70
8	8	16	24	32	40	48	56	64	72	80
9	9	18	27	36	45	54	63	72	81	90
10	10	20	30	40	50	60	70	80	90	100

B

×	2	4	3	1	5	10	6	8	7	9
5	10	20	15	5	25	50	30	40	35	45
3	6	12	9	3	15	30	18	24	21	27
1	2	4	3	1	5	10	6	8	7	9
4	8	16	12	4	20	40	24	32	28	36
2	4	8	6	2	10	20	12	16	14	18
7	14	28	21	7	35	70	42	56	49	63
9	18	36	27	9	45	90	54	72	63	81
10	20	40	30	10	50	100	60	80	70	90
8	16	32	24	8	40	80	48	64	56	72
6	12	24	18	6	30	60	36	48	42	54

C

×	8	6	4	9	7	9	6	7	4	8
5	40	30	20	45	35	45	30	35	20	40
3	24	18	12	27	21	27	18	21	12	24
2	16	12	8	18	14	18	12	14	8	16
3	24	18	12	27	21	27	18	21	12	24
5	40	30	20	45	35	45	30	35	20	40
9	72	54	36	81	63	81	54	63	36	72
4	32	24	16	36	28	36	24	28	16	32
7	56	42	28	63	49	63	42	49	28	56
6	48	36	24	54	42	54	36	42	24	48
8	64	48	32	72	56	72	48	56	32	64

D

×	6	7	8	7	8	6	7	8	6	8
2	12	14	16	14	16	12	14	16	12	16
3	18	21	24	21	24	18	21	24	18	24
4	24	28	32	28	32	24	28	32	24	32
5	30	35	40	35	40	30	35	40	30	40
7	42	49	56	49	56	42	49	56	42	56
8	48	56	64	56	64	48	56	64	48	64
6	36	42	48	42	48	36	42	48	36	48
9	54	63	72	63	72	54	63	72	54	72
8	48	56	64	56	64	48	56	64	48	64
6	36	42	48	42	48	36	42	48	36	48

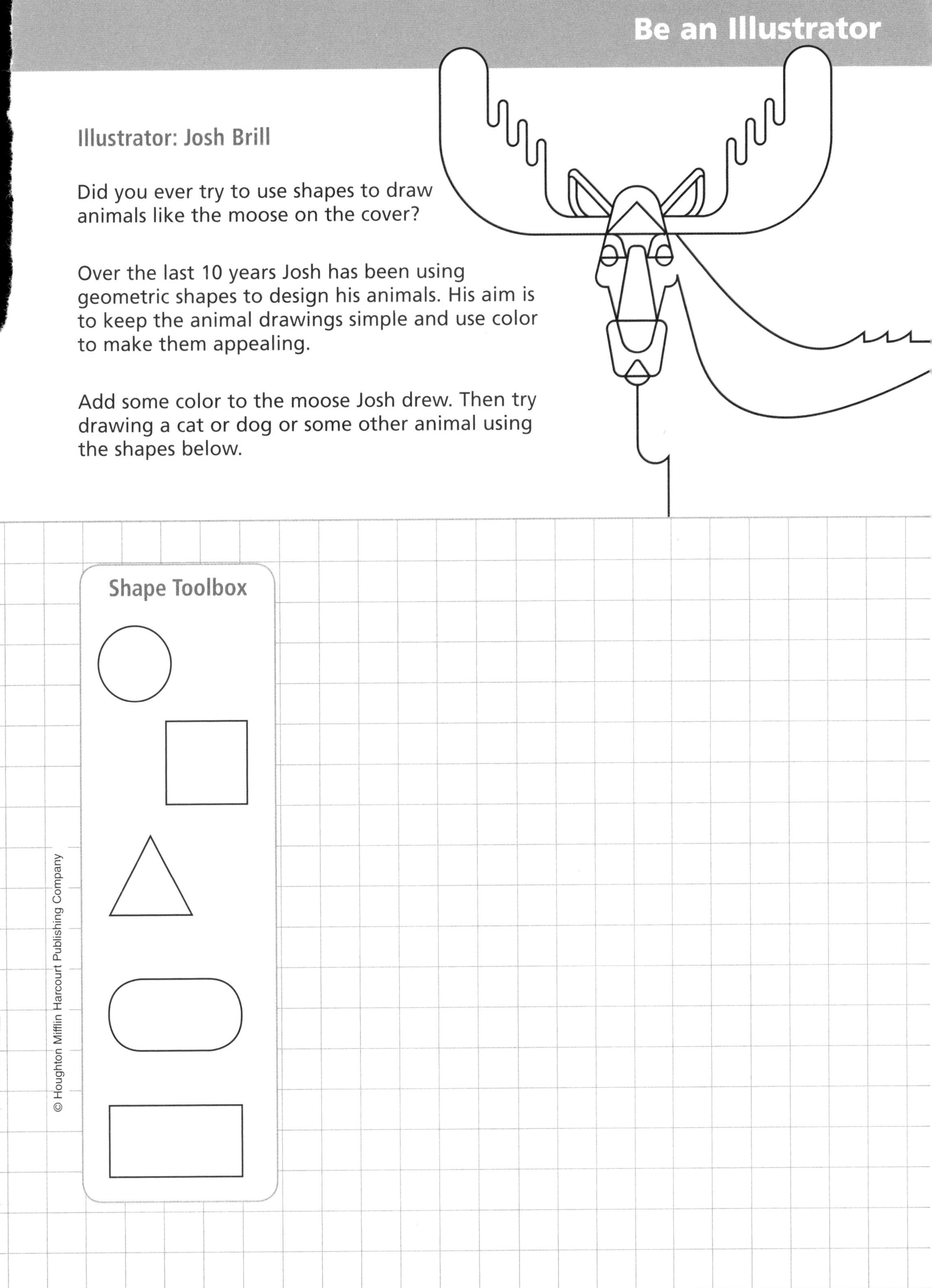

Illustrator: Josh Brill

Did you ever try to use shapes to draw animals like the moose on the cover?

Over the last 10 years Josh has been using geometric shapes to design his animals. His aim is to keep the animal drawings simple and use color to make them appealing.

Add some color to the moose Josh drew. Then try drawing a cat or dog or some other animal using the shapes below.

Shape Toolbox